EVE

Summersdale Publishers Ltd
46 West Street
Chichester
West Sussex
PO19 1RP
UK

www.summersdale.com

Printed and bound in Great Britain.

ISBN 1 84024 378 3

Image Credits
The images on page 67 MS. Bodl. 264, fol. 133v and page 137 Douce Portfolio 136, item 157 'Baby in a high chair' are reproduced courtesy of the Bodleian Library, University of Oxford. The pictures on pages 42, 98, 103, 133, 152, 163, 173, 179, 224 and 226 are reproduced courtesy of the Tate, London, 2003. The pictures on pages 32, 44, 65, 66, 73, 76, 80, 118, 125, 135, 169, 197, 198 and 233 are reproduced courtesy of the Wellcome Library, London.

EVE

SEX, CHILDBIRTH AND MOTHERHOOD THROUGH THE AGES

PETRINA BROWN

summersdale

Dedicated to my mother Irene, with love and admiration,
and my late grandmother Rose, with much love

– CONTENTS –

– INTRODUCTION –

MOTHERHOOD BRINGS GREAT joy to many women, yet it is probably one of the greatest challenges they will ever have to face. Bringing a new life into the world is wonderful, but also terrifying; the awe of responsibility, the overwhelming love. No mother can ever forget the marvel of holding a new life in her arms, or the remarkable experience of giving birth.

Throughout history the most important contribution a woman had to offer society was the 'fruit of her womb'. Many changes have taken place through the centuries, and women now have more control than ever before over this fundamental part of their lives. Most Western women today have the power to choose when to start a family and to determine how large that family will be; pregnancy is often delayed until financial security is achieved. A woman can choose either to have her baby at home or in hospital, and, with the increased number of elective Caesareans in recent years, she may even decide when to have her baby, to fit conveniently into a busy schedule. She may give birth standing, squatting, lying down, or even under water.

Most importantly, women are able to enter motherhood with the confidence that both they and their infants are likely to survive the trauma of birth and reap the benefits of excellent healthcare thereafter. As their due date approaches, many women still feel apprehensive, but no one actually expects to die. Instead, birth plans are discussed with midwives and various pain-relieving methods are considered.

Attitudes towards birth have changed dramatically over the past fifty years, largely due to the sophistication of modern medicine. Women today expect not only to live through the birth, but also to enjoy the experience. Expert technology in surgical techniques, pain-killing drugs and hygienic surroundings are relied upon and even taken for granted.

In addition to advice from healthcare professionals, women are able to consult a wealth of literature on every aspect of pregnancy and childbirth. Most popular in recent years have been natural birth books. Many women feel that they miss out on a rewarding experience if they have a 'managed' birth. Yet for centuries women had no choice but to experience a natural birth. It seems that now the tide is turning and less intervention is sought after. Some women feel that the pursuit of a pain-free labour institutionalises and dehumanises the birth experience. Birth is now not only a safe process, but also a clinical event. There are many questions about natural birth that are not answered in the vast supply of birthing manuals. What was childbirth really like in all those long years before modern medical technology and the successful Caesarean section? Has too much been sacrificed in the search for safe, pain-free delivery?

The truth is that until recently childbirth and motherhood could be very hard for women. For some, childbearing was constant and debilitating, and it won them little respect. Looking at the prehistoric and ancient world as a whole, it is clear that the responsibilities placed on women by society could only have increased their anxieties as they approached motherhood. Pain and possible death coupled with superstition and medical ignorance must have obliterated any joy felt at bringing new life into the world. All too often men, driven by fear rather than malice, ostracised women at a time when they most needed support. Few men became involved in the birth process until the rise of the male midwife in the late seventeenth and early eighteenth century. A legacy of suspicion, often fuelled by strongly held religious conviction, was passed down from generation to generation.

This suspicion meant that for centuries women relied upon other more experienced women to assist them during labour. Midwives successfully delivered many children if the birth was straightforward. When complications arose, however, there was often little that could be done to assist a safe delivery. Without the use of instruments, a local midwife dealing with an obstructed labour might have little choice but to pull on whatever part of the baby she could get hold of. An observer of a birth in 1752 wrote: 'If the midwife finds any unusual presentation she becomes confused and [...] begins to pull, even if it is a polyp growing to the uterus, whereby often the mother pays with her life.' In the absence of a safe alternative, the midwife would sometimes use violent physical action, holding the labouring woman upside down or shaking her vigorously. If all else failed she may even have abandoned the woman to her fate or, equally horrific, summoned the local barber-surgeon, who would get to work using hooks and knives.

If a woman was safely delivered she remained vulnerable due to the risk of death from infection or haemorrhage. Hygiene was not yet a priority as the connection between bacteria and infection was not made until the end of the nineteenth century. To compound the situation, fresh air was regarded with terror, and the birthing chamber was arranged to be free from any draughts.

Bernard Faust, a male midwife, wrote in 1784: 'How marvellous it is when mothers leave the windows of their bedrooms open. Then the stand-offish old women, who otherwise crowd round the mother in a room they have heated to boiling point, will now stay home, for they dread these cool rooms, cleansed with fresh air, more fearfully than if one were burning asafetida [a foul-smelling gum resin].'

Those women who were fortunate enough to survive birth and the dangerous days that followed faced an even more challenging task – ensuring the survival of their newly delivered infant. What happened if a mother lost her breast milk? What was used as an alternative and how was it fed to the baby? What was used to keep a baby dry before the introduction of nappies?

In *Eve* I have drawn together details from many centuries of history to create an overall picture of birth and babycare. I have chosen to focus mainly on Britain, Europe and America, since they have been most influential in contributing to safer ante- and postnatal care. The poems and quotes scattered throughout the book help to convey just how dramatic the changes in birth and babycare have been and provide a personal perspective from mothers in the past. Clearly the one overriding question in the minds of women as their pains began was, 'Will I survive?'

1

'IF WE COULD SURVIVE WITHOUT A WIFE ...'

– THE CLASSICAL WORLD –

M ANY QUESTIONS ARISE when considering how women in ancient societies coped with the process of pregnancy and childbirth. What happened when things went wrong? Who helped deliver? How was the infant cared for? What happened when a pregnancy was unwanted? Since the earliest writings only emerged from Egypt and Mesopotamia around 3000 BC, details of how early societies dealt with matters such as pregnancy and childbirth are largely a matter of conjecture, although archaeological relics provide valuable clues on which to base assumptions.

Urbanisation began in the Middle East; people began to group themselves into societies and build houses of mud and reeds close to one another, the forerunner to our modern towns and cities. One of the world's earliest cities was discovered at Catal Huyuk in central Turkey. The city flourished around 6150 BC, and in its ruins a fine clay statuette was found. This depicted a goddess supported by two leopards as she crouched between them while giving birth. We can surmise from this that women of the time generally squatted during labour.

The best-preserved medical texts from ancient times are those of the Greeks and Romans, who separated the art of the physician from that of the priest, laying the foundations of modern medicine. Of particular interest are works by Galen, a physician and philosopher born in AD 131, and by Soranus of Ephesus, a physician practising in Rome in the second century AD. These early texts provide colourful and detailed information on the care of childbearing women in the classical world.

Roman and Greek medical knowledge was extensive, although some of their theories were erroneous; however, without anaesthetics, antibiotics or pain relievers, the practical help offered to women in childbirth was limited. Particular methods of dealing with the problems associated with reproduction were developed, and the rituals and superstitions that were passed from generation to generation played a large part in people's lives. From the moment of conception through to caring for and feeding a new infant, the behaviour of mothers was governed not only by medical advice from experts, but also to a large extent by the rituals and customs particular to the society and region in which they lived.

Women as Childbearers
Many early religions placed women in an honoured position; their nurturing and caring qualities were admired, and their ability to carry offspring was considered miraculous. However, as patriarchal nomadic tribes, such as the Celts, became dominant in Europe from around 5000 BC, belief systems began to change.

With the spread of patriarchal religions, birth was no longer seen as a miraculous event that women had the honour of participating in, but as a curse from Almighty God. The book of Genesis tells us that God said to Eve: 'I will greatly multiply thy sorrow and thy conception; in sorrow thou shalt bring forth children; and thy desire shall be to thy husband, and he shall rule over thee.'

A common thread running through most religions appeared to be the close connection between women and the natural cycle of life and death. Birth was viewed as negative because it always ultimately ended in death, and womankind was considered to be responsible.

In ancient Israel women were forbidden from entering the temple and had to confine themselves away from their husband for seven days after menstruation. Leviticus 15:19-20 states: 'If a woman has an issue, and her issue in her flesh be blood, she shall be put apart for seven days: and whosoever toucheth her shall be unclean until the even and everything that she lieth upon in her separation shall be unclean.'

This feminine 'pollution' extended beyond menstruation to include pregnancy, when women were generally thought to be extremely unclean. Since our earliest recorded history women have suffered hardship during pregnancy and childbirth, and have also had to accept society's judgement of them as unclean.

Lack of understanding of the female body and reproductive system caused many problems. Men were often frightened of a menstruating woman and avoided contact with her at all costs during this time. It was thought that women were unbalanced, irrational, and occasionally mad. This insanity apparently sometimes arose from the breasts. According to the 'Father of Medicine' Hippocrates: 'There is a thick vein in each breast. These contain the greatest portion of intelligence [...] in one who is about to go mad the following is a warning indication: blood collects in the breasts.' When women did not conform to expected behaviour, perhaps while pre-menstrual, it was easy to assume they had gone mad, and, of course, during menstruation the breasts do become engorged.

In the few Greek and Roman manuscripts dedicated to women's health much is written about hysteria, literally, 'wombiness'. The womb was believed to move around the body, causing ill health and insanity. Aretaeus of Cappadocia, a physician who practised in Rome and Alexandria in the second century AD, described the womb as 'an independent animal', which 'likes fragrant smells and moves towards them, but dislikes foul odours and moves away from them'. All manner of illnesses were thought to be the result of the wandering womb, and in his medical manuscripts Aretaeus wrote that these disorders could be remedied by 'foul smells, and also pleasant fragrances applied to the vagina'.

> If we could survive without a wife, citizens of Rome, all of us would do without that nuisance; but since nature has so decreed that we cannot manage comfortably with them, nor live in any way without them [...] we must plan for our lasting preservation rather than for our temporary pleasure.
>
> – Emperor Augustus addressing the Senate, 17 BC

Some Greek doctors, Galen in particular, assumed that a human female body worked in the same way as a female animal's body, and since they dissected animals they believed their knowledge was accurate. The Greek historian Strabo recorded that physicians sometimes removed a woman's ovaries in order to preserve her slim figure, thus plunging her into premature menopause. Women were very rarely examined internally, and throughout the entire Hippocratic corpus vaginal examinations are mentioned only twice.

While the ancient Romans and Egyptians saw women as the creators of life, and so also of death, in Greece men were seen as the transmitters of life, a female body being merely a weaker version of the male. Aristotle describes the female of the species in *Historia Animalium* as a 'misbegotten male', although ironically it is now known that all embryos are female when first formed. The Greeks also thought that men brought health and sanity to women through intercourse, causing the women to menstruate and thereby relieve the build-up of blood around the heart.

Fertility

From the beginning of human history procreation has been the ultimate goal of both man and woman to ensure the survival of their genes. According to the Old Testament, God spoke to Noah when the waters of the flood had subsided. He wanted all humans and animals to 'be fruitful and multiply upon the earth'. Our early ancestors certainly appreciated the importance of fertility for the future of civilisation, but they were unsure as to exactly how a woman became pregnant, and therefore placed great faith in fertility gods and goddesses, and rituals.

Correspondingly, medical advisers made many assumptions about the workings of the reproductive system which were often completely inaccurate. Men in Rome were encouraged to take care of their diet so as to ensure fertile sperm. Galen recommended men eat chickpeas, onions, octopus and pine nuts; in fact, any food that produced flatulence, since the best sperm was thought to contain plenty of air. Men were also warned strongly against wasting their sperm, which was believed to contain a vital life force called *pneuma*. If too much *pneuma* was used up in a degrading lifestyle, men would be sapped of their life spirit and would become weak. Sperm was believed to be blood that gradually became white as it reached the testicles.

In his medical text *Gynaecology*, written in the second century AD, Soranus advised men to choose their women wisely: 'from the ages of fifteen to forty [...] not too manish, compact, oversturdy or too flabby and very moist', in order to ensure 'one's best shot at producer of offspring'. Features to look out for in a fertile mate were a good-sized head and big eyes, although not too large. Small heads and eyes, particularly when accompanied by protruding foreheads, were to be avoided. The advice did not stop there. Various methods of lovemaking were recommended if conception was desired, and a snack followed by a good rub down before the act was considered to be advantageous.

As in some countries today, in Roman times a male heir was the goal of many married couples. Some practitioners believed that the level of heat during lovemaking determined the outcome of whether the offspring would be male or female. Galen, on the other hand, believed that the co-mingling of male sperm from the testes and female 'sperm' from the woman's ovary at the moment of orgasm produced a new life, and males were produced when sperm from the right testicle mixed with 'sperm' from the right ovary.

Other assumptions were made in Roman times about the connection between the circumstances surrounding conception and the resulting child. It was thought, for example, that a child's personality could be affected by alcohol, and women were therefore advised to ensure sobriety during coitus, in case the soul of the new infant became 'the victim of strange fantasies'.

In this new millennium, we rely more on medical technology than on myths and legends, but in the absence of freely available medical care women placed their trust in traditional ideas. If a woman in ancient times was unable to conceive, she no doubt felt as frustrated as any woman today in the same position. The drive to create a new life is a very strong biological urge and infertility can cause deep heartache. When a couple want to start a family, prolonged failure to conceive can be devastating.

Just as couples today who are unable to conceive seek other ways of having a much longed for child, so too our ancestors sought solutions elsewhere. In ancient Israel, for example, it was customary, in accordance with Jewish law, for a woman to offer a slave girl to her husband if she was unable to bear him a child. According to the Bible, Rachel was barren, and she therefore gave her maidservant to her husband Jacob, to 'go in unto her; and she shall bear upon my knees, that I may also have children by her'. An early example of surrogacy which, due to widespread slavery, was a widely accepted alternative in those days.

Early records such as this demonstrate that fertility, or a lack of it, often dominated people's lives; some women went to desperate lengths in order to have a child, while many others struggled to control the number of pregnancies they had to endure.

The First Contraceptives

Without effective methods of birth control, fertile women throughout history suffered almost continuous pregnancies and then had to cope with the consequences. It is not surprising that many sought a reprieve by taking any and every contraceptive concoction available to them. A great variety of superstitions evolved in an effort to control fertility, and contraceptive recipes were also developed, despite a lack of precise medical knowledge.

A number of plants with powerful contraceptive qualities were known in the classical world, and our ancestors took full advantage of them. A common contraceptive used in Mediterranean countries was silphium, a plant native to North Africa. This plant provided a large income for the North African city of Cyrene and actually appeared on its coins in recognition of this. Pennyroyal was another plant popularly used for birth control, and it is referred to in Aristophanes' comedy *Peace*, first performed in 421 BC. One of the characters in the play is worried that his female companion may become pregnant, and his friend remarks, 'not if you add a dose of pennyroyal'. Recent studies have confirmed the effectiveness of this plant in preventing conception.

Hippocratic writings dating back to 430 BC mention the use of pomegranate as a contraceptive, and it is now known to be effective in preventing conception. Other preventatives were less savoury:

an Egyptian manuscript dated around 1850 BC describes the use of a pessary made from a paste of crocodile dung.

The Romans' methods of contraception were so successful that birth levels became very low. Adultery was common, men regularly used prostitutes instead of relying on their wives for sexual satisfaction, and, consequently, married couples probably had little sexual contact with each other. The Emperor Augustus became so concerned about the birth crisis that in 18 BC he promulgated new laws in an effort to encourage procreation, offering tax incentives to married couples and later criminalising adultery. The punishments for adultery were severe: a father was permitted to kill his daughter and a husband could kill his wife's lover and divorce her if adultery was suspected. Augustus's own daughter Julia was exiled to the island of Pandateria following charges of adultery.

The Romans had regular sexual relations, even if not always within marriage, so how then did they control the birth rate so successfully? It was largely because prostitutes were well versed in the art of contraception and, via their clients, this knowledge filtered through to ordinary women in bedrooms throughout Rome.

Their methods included the use of potions, sometimes as contraceptives but also as abortifacients. The low birth rate suggests that these prescriptions were extremely effective.

Some contraceptives may have been effective not specifically because of the ingredients they contained, but due to the advice given with them. It was advised, for example, that ground leaves of barren wort be taken after menstruation in order to prevent conception for the next five days. A woman is most infertile just after menstruation, well before ovulation, and would therefore have been unlikely to get pregnant during this time anyway.

Aristotle noted that many pregnancies were avoided 'by anointing the part of the womb on which the seed falls with oil of cedar, ointment of lead or frankincense co-mingled with olive oil'. He probably did not realise that the oil had the effect of blocking the entry of sperm into the uterus, but he appreciated that its use was effective. The use of olive oil was widespread in Greece and Rome; it was burnt in lamps, used in cooking and even made into soap, consequently it was available to everyone.

Early Contraceptive Potions

In order to prevent conception, drink male or female fern root in sweet-tasting wine, the blossom and leaves of the willow, and cabbage blossoms in wine after coitus.

– Oribasius, *Librium Incertium*, fourth century AD

Cyreanic sap, the sip of a pea in two glasses of winy water: to be drunk once a month. This also causes the onset of menstruation. Or else, cyreanic sap, oppanax, rue leaves in equal part: triturate, mix with some sap. Take an amount the size of a bean and drink with winy water.

– Aetios of Amida, *Tetrabiblion*, sixth century AD

The finely ground leaves of the willow taken with water, iron rust, iron slag. The root of barren wort or bishop's hat, *Epimediendum Alpinum L* or *Botrychium Lunaria* – the plant has not with certainty been identified – causes sterility; when the finely ground leaves of this plant are taken to the amount of five drachms in wine after menstruation, they prevent conception for the duration of five days. The roots of the brake or fern are given to women to prevent conception; if taken by a pregnant woman they cause miscarriage. Two drachms of Ostracite drunk for each day four days after menstruation will prevent conception.

– Dioscorides, *De materia medica*, first century AD

Pessaries were another method of contraception that worked on the same basis as oil. In *De materia medica* the first century AD herbalist Dioscorides prescribed sticky mixtures of peppermint, cedar gum, alum and axeweed in honey. Soranus' textbook of obstetrics, *Gynaecology*, provided extensive guidance and recommendations on how to avoid conception and was used throughout Europe right up until the sixteenth century. Soranus also advocated the use of pessaries and advised women to 'smear the orifice of the uterus all over with olive oil or honey or cedar resin or juice of the balsam tree, alone or together with white lead; or with a moist cerate containing myrtle oil and white lead; or before the act with moist alum, or with galbanum together with wine; or to put a lock of fine wool into the orifice of the uterus'.

Although this technique may have been a good preventative measure, it is clear that Soranus did not understand how it worked as he suggests that the suppositories could be removed before intercourse if desired. It was generally thought that the pessary's contraceptive power lay in its ability to cool and so shut off the womb, thereby protecting it against pregnancy. Soranus obviously appreciated the potency of herbs, however, and often warned women of the possible side effects of using pungent substances. They could expect to experience stomach ulcers, nausea and congestion of the head if they were regular users of his prescriptions.

Another method advocated by Soranus, and one which could not possibly cause side effects, was an ancient form of *coitus interruptus*. 'During the sexual act, at the critical moment of coitus when the man is about to discharge his seed, the woman must hold her breath and draw away a little, so that the seed may not be hurled too deep into the cavity of the uterus. Getting up immediately and squatting down slowly she should induce sneezing and carefully wipe the vagina all around; she might even drink something cold.' The notion that if a woman does not experience orgasm and tightens her vaginal muscles she will not conceive still persists today.

Despite their sophistication and considerable obstetric skills, many Romans still placed great faith in superstition and ritual. Dioscorides developed contraceptive prescriptions that revealed a distinct lack of knowledge of the workings of the female body: 'The menstrual blood of women seems to prevent conception when they spread themselves with it, when they step over it [...] asparagus tied up as an amulet or drunk as a decoction will prevent conception and render one sterile.'

Pliny the Elder, in his *Historia Naturalis*, offered the following advice:

> A lizard drowned in a man's urine has the effect of an antaphrodisiac upon the person whose urine it is [...] the testes of a game-cock rubbed with goose grease and attached to the body in a ram's skin have the effect of an antaphrodisiac; the same too will the testes of any dunghill cock, placed together with the blood of a cock, beneath the bed [...] if a man makes water upon a dog's urine he will be similarly disinclined to copulation.

Aetios of Amida, a Byzantine Greek physician, likewise suggested: 'Wear a cat liver in a tube on the left foot, or wear the testicles of a cat in a tube around the umbilicus [the navel]. The woman should carry as an amulet around the anus the tooth of a child or a glass from a marble quarry.'

It is safe to assume that the majority of these potions were utterly useless, except perhaps psychologically. Any man who has ripped the liver or testicles from a cat is unlikely to feel romantically inclined towards his wife, particularly as she was supposed to wear one of these items about her person.

If a man chose to, there were concoctions available for him to use in order to avoid conception. Dioscorides recommended the use of the herb periklymenon, tentatively identified as honeysuckle, and claimed that if a man used it for thirty-seven days he would become barren. He also suggested applying ointments to the tip of the penis, an ancient form of spermicide.

Other attempts were made to divert semen, such as the process of infibulation, whereby the foreskin was pulled down over the penis and held in place with a metal ring.

Abortion – As Old as Life

Termination of pregnancy has been used as a means of controlling family size for thousands of years. The ways in which women in the classical world attempted to procure abortion were horrendous, painful and probably ineffective: scalding hot baths, falling down stairs or binding their abdomens tightly. Various measures discussed by Roman doctors included rigorous exercise, pessaries, injections of warm oil and rue, and poultices of linseed, fenugreek, mallow and wormwood. The Romans also possessed a very good knowledge of the power of plants, and Dioscorides knew of more than twenty-five plants that could cause a woman to have an abortion.

Soranus provided elaborate details to women who wished to terminate a pregnancy. He advised them to follow the opposite advice that he usually gave to women who wanted to prevent a miscarriage. They were firstly to either walk or ride a horse energetically, jump and carry heavy loads, then take a diuretic potion, such as one made from asparagus, to encourage menstruation. He recommended following this with daily warm baths, soaking for a long time, drinking wine and eating pungent food. A mixture of linseed, fenugreek, marshmallow and artemesia could be added to the bath water, and further potency could be added by applying a plaster composed of the same substances then adding old olive oil, honey or rue juice. If the pregnancy persisted, a strong plaster made of lupine meal, ox bile and wormwood was suggested. Exact proportions are not mentioned in ancient texts, perhaps because vendors wished to keep the precise recipes secret so as to assure them of future business. All the ingredients mentioned, with the exception of linseed, were also used as contraceptives, and were seen as the first step to try to abort a pregnancy.

If the woman's condition remained unchanged she could follow a harsher regime, using more powerful drugs. Soranus advised the use of myrtle, wallflower and bitter lupines in equal quantities, mixed with water and moulded into tablets, and if this produced bleeding the woman should be shaken rigorously on horseback. Interestingly, lupine is now known to cause uterine contractions and can abort pregnancy in guinea pigs, even in the second half of their term. Wormwood also appeared in early prescriptions as an abortifacient, and is known today as a poisonous plant that can cause miscarriage. It also has contraceptive qualities as it delays ovulation and prevents sperm implantation.

Abortion was not illegal in Rome, but many doctors, including Soranus, would only terminate a pregnancy in women whose life would otherwise be in danger. Abortion was only considered to be a crime if carried out against the husband's wishes. There is archaeological evidence that the surgical removal of fetuses occurred in the classical world, but it is believed to have been a rare event.

Sadly, if both contraceptive and abortion prescriptions failed, many poor families dealt with the problem of excess children by either selling or killing them following birth. It was common for infants to be exposed and left to die alone. Abandoned newborns fared better in Egypt than elsewhere as the Egyptians rarely left any child to die; if any abandoned infants were found they were taken in and given the name Koprey, meaning 'off the dunghill'. Jews were also opposed to exposure, regarding it a crime to kill a child. In Rome infanticide was only classed as a crime towards the end of the fourth century AD by joint emperors Valentinian and Gratian.

Despite the abandonment of these babies, the behaviour of their parents was no doubt a result of their desperate circumstances, and not undertaken lightly. It is perhaps easier to understand their actions when you consider that even today, with a wide network of support and social benefits, newborns are occasionally abandoned in the streets by frightened young mothers. How much more difficult life must have been in ancient communities, when being poor meant being unable to eat. No doubt parents nursed the hope, however unlikely, that their baby would be found and adopted.

With-child

Soranus and his contemporaries believed that if a woman was able to hold on to the male seed she would feel shivery after intercourse and become pregnant. She could also expect to have swollen breasts, and her arms and legs would feel heavy.

Most of the antenatal care in the first few months focused on retaining the male seed within the womb, which was seen as vital if the pregnancy was to continue. There were many dangers to avoid if the seed was not to be dislodged, including, 'forced detention of breath, coughing, sneezing, blows and falls, lifting heavy weights, leaping, sitting on hard chairs, want, drunkenness and flow of blood from the nose'.

Maintaining the seed within the womb could be aided by anointing the woman with freshly pressed oil from unripe olives. At the first signs of pregnancy it was also recommended that the woman rest in bed for two days on a diet of grains, and then she should not bathe or drink wine in case the seed was weakened. Sexual intercourse was strictly forbidden. After approximately forty days it was thought that the second pregnancy stage, called *pica*, was entered. The symptoms accompanying this stage were nausea, upset stomach, fever, dizziness, and cravings for unusual foods such as 'earth, charcoal, tendrils, and acid fruit'. A good rubdown was suggested to alleviate such problems, along with plain food and a tightly wrapped girdle.

Soranus believed the next stage of pregnancy began four months later and a woman should eat more food, take more exercise and get more sleep in preparation for the birth. Linen bandages were suggested for the final two months as a support to bear the additional weight of the baby. Soranus thought that the genitals should also be prepared for the feat ahead and suggested regular injections of oil such as softened goose fat into the vagina, followed by the application of herbs. (Similarly, modern mothers are advised that in the weeks leading up to labour, it can be helpful to lubricate the skin surrounding the vagina through the application of oils, but thankfully the ingredients are now a little more appealing.)

Although pleased to have successfully reached the end of her pregnancy without miscarrying, it must have been with considerable trepidation that a woman in the ancient world approached her labour, and the inevitable agonies that would accompany it.

'In Birth Pangs ...'

Throughout the classical world taboos forbidding association and contact with a woman in childbirth were rife. This can only have added to the fear that women suffered as their labour began. They not only anticipated an agonising labour with little or no pain relief, but also faced the very real possibility of not surviving long enough to hold the baby in their arms.

It is not surprising then that many myths developed in relation to childbirth. Women in the ancient world turned to powerful goddesses associated with childbirth for comfort and reassurance during labour. Faith in these protective goddesses must have served to alleviate at least some of the stress during each woman's travail.

The Egyptians had great confidence in their deities, and the goddesses of childbirth were particularly esteemed and worshipped by the common people. The goddess Taweret had the head of a hippopotamus, the legs and arms of a lion, the tail of a crocodile and large drooping human breasts. Many amulets featuring her have been found, showing how great the demand for her protection was. Vessels have also been discovered, moulded in her shape, with holes in the nipples through which the milk poured out.

Hathor, the Egyptian patroness of lovers, was thought to help women to conceive and give birth. Meskhenet, whose symbol was a tile, representing the bricks on which Egyptian women squatted to give birth, was thought to be a sacred midwife, ensuring safe delivery. People believed the ram-headed god Khnum made each child and its *ka*, or spirit double, on a potter's wheel, then put it into the mother's body.

Many cultures adopted the use of special rituals in order to cope with the pain and peril of childbirth, although the most detailed records are to be found in Roman medical manuals. Soranus recorded information that contained very little superstition, an unusual feature of documents from this age. In his manuals he argued that midwives should be well-educated women with a good knowledge of obstetrics and paediatric care. He taught rational midwifery based on knowledge, not superstition, preferring women to be treated with kindness rather than brute force.

There is some evidence to suggest that midwives from the eastern, Hellenised Mediterranean were more knowledgeable than those in Rome. Some advanced to the position of obstetrician after formal training, and even authored gynaecological manuals. It is thought that rich families in Rome may have sent for these specially trained midwives to attend to their young mothers when the need arose.

While these midwives were generally well educated, it appears that most midwives practising in Rome were originally slaves. They usually managed to improve their status through the work that they did, and often gained their freedom in this way.

Besides being generally well respected, midwives were probably well paid; in the play *Miles Gloriosus* by Plautus, the character Periplectomenus complained that the midwife was demanding more money despite the fact that he had already paid her. Soranus warned midwives not to be too greedy, and some legal records suggest that their pay was similar to that of male doctors. Poorer families who were unable to meet the fees of a midwife employed the services of wise women called *sagae* to help them through the ordeal of labour.

If a midwife could read she probably would have studied the medical texts prepared by Soranus, who had very definite ideas as to the procedures that must be followed to ensure a successful birth. He felt that the labouring woman should be placed in a comfortable environment and that the midwife should have adequate instruments at her disposal:

Olive oil (not previously used for cooking)
Warm water and ointments
Soft sea sponges
Pieces of wool bandages (for swaddling)
A pillow on which to lay the newborn
Pennyroyal, barley, groats, apples, quinces, lemons, melons, cucumbers (to smell)
A birthing chair
A hard bed on which to deliver the baby
A soft bed for the mother to rest on

The birthing chair is described in great detail in the manuals, and its use was regarded as important; it was felt that the optimum position for delivery was upright, and women of the time almost always gave birth standing, sitting, or crouching. From the description given it would seem that the chair was very similar to those used today. There was usually a crescent-shaped hole in the chair through which the baby would be delivered, and armrests at the side for gripping and resting on. Some chairs had sturdy backs for the woman to lean against, but occasionally midwives used a stool and an attendant would stand behind the labouring woman to support her back. If a midwife could not afford a stool it was recommended that the mother-to-be should sit on another woman's lap and deliver the baby through her open legs.

A woman would only move to the chair for the final stage of labour, in order to actually deliver the baby. At the onset of labour she would lie on the hard bed with her feet drawn up and her thighs parted. Soranus recommended that the midwife relieve some of the woman's pain by laying a cloth soaked in warm olive oil over her abdomen and placing bladders filled with warm olive oil against her sides.

While the cervix dilated Soranus thought it was advantageous for the midwife to soak her finger in oil and gently rub to increase the opening. When almost ready to deliver, the woman would move to the birthing stool, providing she felt strong enough to get up. Three additional assistants were required to help the midwife, one to stand on either side of the chair and one at the back. Soranus suggested they should be strong enough to support the woman and also be of calm temperament, 'capable of gently allaying the anxiety'. The assistant at the back of the chair had the additional task of holding a cloth at the labouring woman's anus to prevent haemorrhoids appearing, a practice still followed by modern midwives today.

The assistants at the side of the chair had to gently push down on the abdomen to help expel the child while the midwife, who sat in front of the mother, would encourage her and remind her to focus on her breathing. Soranus advised midwives to wear cloth coverings on their hands so as not to drop the slippery newborn as they gently pulled on the infant's body.

The focus throughout the manuals remained on the care of the mother. It was seen as vital to keep her calm and relaxed, and Soranus notes that when a mother experienced excessive 'grief, joy, fear, timidity, lack of energy, anger, or extreme indulgence', her pain was much greater. Midwives who followed his advice were caring and sympathetic. Their aim was to make the birth as comfortable and untraumatic as possible, and it seems they were very attentive to the labouring woman.

> When the natal hour of toil-bearing Hercules was near [...] seven nights and days I [Alcmena] was in torture [...] There cruel Juno sat [...] listening to my groans, with her right knee crossed over her left, and with her fingers interlocked; and so she stayed the birth [...] and prevented my deliverance.
>
> – Ovid, *Metamorphoses IX*, AD 8

> To sit by a pregnant woman, or by a person to whom any remedy is being administered, with the fingers of one hand inserted between those of another, acts as a magic spell; a discovery that was made, it is said, when Alcmena was delivered of Hercules. If the fingers are thus joined, clasping one or both knees, or if the ham of one leg is first put upon the knee of the other, and then changed about, the omen is of still worse signification. Hence it is, that in councils held by generals and persons in authority, our ancestors forbade these postures as being an impediment to all business.
>
> – Pliny the Elder, *Historia Naturalis*, AD 77

It was believed that the delivery of a baby could be obstructed by the crossing of legs or tying of knots. Consequently, if a woman appeared to be experiencing difficulties, doors were opened, hair untied and even cattle set free in an attempt to help her.

Most women in Rome were attended throughout their labour by a midwife, unless the birth was particularly difficult, in which case a male physician would take over. Soranus suggested that the infant could be extracted during a difficult labour by 'placing nooses or ropes circularly round the arms or other parts of the fetus', with the other end of the ropes fixed around knobs that projected from the chair.

Medieval illustration of the birth of Julius Caesar by Caesarean section

Another method used to pull the baby out was 'version'. The main aim of version was to turn the baby from an awkward position to one which would facilitate an easier birth. It involved inserting a hand, between contractions, and literally manoeuvring the baby down. It was an extremely dangerous procedure for both mother and baby, and excruciatingly painful for the mother. Not surprisingly, many women were hard to convince that version should be carried out, preferring to die rather than face such agony, however other options were limited.

Caesareans would have been avoided because a woman could never have survived such an operation. It was once thought that Caesareans were so called because Julius Caesar was born in this way; however, ancient sources prove that this could not be accurate as his mother Aurelia lived to be an adviser to her grown son, and without anaesthesia she would have surely died during the operation.

Soranus was determined to try and make childbirth as safe as possible, and he did not approve of superstitions or the use of folk medicine during childbirth, which he thought interfered with the process. He was careful 'not to overlook salutary measures on account of a dream or omen or some customary rite.'

Pliny the Elder's approach to childbirth was distinctly different from that of Soranus, believing as he did in the use of charms to hasten and ease labour. It is easy to understand the objections of a physician such as Soranus when examining the recommendations from those who practised folk medicine. Pliny, for instance, advises the use of hyena's feet, snake sloughs (shed skin), canine placentas, and vulture feathers, which must have greatly increased the risk of infection for the mother, particularly as these items were often placed on or around her body. These practices seem bizarre today, but any mother whose labour was approaching knew it would be an agonising experience and would no doubt cling to anything that might offer relief, however repulsive. It is also important not to underestimate the power of suggestion. If a labouring woman was told that having a snake's slough tied to her thigh would take away some of the pain she was suffering, it may have had that precise effect.

Popular Pain Relievers Suggested by Pliny the Elder and Contemporaries

Fumigations with the fat from hyena loins
Wearing the right foot of a hyena (left foot causes death!)
A drink sprinkled with powdered sow's dung
Sow's milk mixed with honey wine
Drinking goose semen mixed with water or liquids that flow from a weasel's uterus through its genitals
Tying a snake's slough to the thigh
Placing the placenta from a dog on the thighs (removing immediately after delivery)
Holding a stick with which a frog has been shaken from a snake
A vulture's feather under the woman's feet
Drinking hedge mustard in tepid wine
Earthworms in raisin wine
Using the membrane from newborn goats, made into wine
Hare's rennet applied with saffron and leek juice

Many relics have been unearthed by archaeologists that confirm some of the methods highlighted in the medical texts. A terracotta plate found in a tomb in Rome shows a labouring woman on a birthing stool, an attendant behind supporting her, and the midwife sitting in front of her trying to pull the baby out. Another plate depicts a similar scene, although showing two men also attending to the woman, perhaps in their role as physicians.

The relics and written documentation combine to depict a gentle, attentive approach to caring for women in labour in Rome, from both midwives and doctors alike. It is difficult to assess exactly how many women and infants lost their lives in the process of childbirth, but in complicated births they would not have fared well, despite the high level of care.

There are numerous records of maternal and infant deaths in ancient documents: Pliny the Elder noted the deaths of both daughters of his friend Helvidius during childbirth; the philanthropist Herodes Atticus of Athens wrote of his terrible grief following the death of his newborn son, only hours old; it is recorded that Julius Caesar's daughter Julia died in childbirth; and according to the Bible, the barren Rachel who gave her handmaid to her husband in order to have a child, eventually fell pregnant but, 'it came to pass, when she was in hard labour, that the midwife said unto her, "Fear not; thou shalt have this son also." And it came to pass, as her soul was in departing (for she died), that she called his name Ben-oni (son of my sorrow).'

After birth

If a woman of Rome was safely delivered she would be cared for by the midwife for a few days after the birth. The midwife would ensure that the mother received adequate rest and also offered advice where needed. If the mother's breasts were sore or engorged there were a number of treatments available, including sponging them with 'mildly contracting things' such as diluted vinegar, or tender dates with bread and diluted vinegar, then applying a close-fitting bandage. Soranus wrote that if tender care of the breasts failed to ease engorgement and they became inflamed, then surgery was required. Apparently the wife of Plutarch, the first century AD philosopher and biographer, was operated on when her nipple became bruised while nursing her baby son. Plutarch commented that she showed 'true mother love', and implied that the surgery was extremely painful for her, which is hardly surprising.

Once again, the advice offered by Soranus on caring for the mother following childbirth differed enormously from the recommendations of Pliny the Elder, an advocate of folk medicine. Since a newly delivered mother was at great risk from infection it would not be surprising if followers of Pliny's suggestions fell ill or even died in their attempts at relieving some of their discomfort.

Folk Remedies for the New Mother to Relieve Sore Breasts

Drink mouse dung diluted with rainwater and ass's milk
Rub breasts with sow's blood, goose grease, rose oil and a spider's web
Use a poultice of partridge egg ash, zinc oxide ointment and wax
Lay earthworms dipped in honey wine on the breasts to draw out pus

---

When the discomfort of the first few days following delivery had eased, a woman would adhere to the customs associated with new mothers in her particular society. These customs differed depending on which religion or society she belonged to, but the rules were universal in one aspect: she was tainted and needed to be cleansed. According to the Bible, if a woman bore a boy she would be unclean for seven days and would need to purify herself for thirty-three days. If she bore a girl, she would be impure for two weeks and would need to purify herself for seventy days. According to Leviticus, thirty to thirty-three days of purgation should follow the birth of a boy, and between forty-two to sixty-six days after the birth of a girl.

This treatment of women was not only based on strongly held religious beliefs, but may also have arisen out of consideration for their welfare. Women may have been shut away firstly in order to enforce rest and recuperation following their exhausting ordeal, relieving them of their usual duties, and secondly, they would have been protected from any infection from the outside world at a time when they were most vulnerable. There were benefits to being shut away from society; apart from being able to enjoy a short period away from work, a new mother in confinement would have been in an ideal position to get to know her new baby with little disturbance, enjoying a quiet time in which to bond.

The Newborn

It must have been with great joy that a new mother in the ancient world held her baby for the first time. All the dangers of the birth behind her, she would have been able to relax and enjoy the moment. The midwife always assessed the baby to make sure that it was worth rearing – if not she may have recommended that it be exposed, a custom especially common in Greece, though also practised in Rome. Soranus recommended some tests that would ascertain the health of the newborn. He suggested that the midwife lay the baby on the ground and if it cried lustily it was a good sign, but a weak cry meant a weak baby. She should also check that the body was normal, with all openings clear, and finally she should test the newborn's senses by touching the skin – if this elicited a response it was regarded as a positive reaction. Not all handicaps were considered unmanageable, however, as there were lame children cared for in Rome, but it may have been impossible to provide the care needed to cope with severely disabled babies in those days.

Spartan parents employed a grim method to test whether their babies would be tough enough to survive – they exposed weak newborns on bleak hillsides. The disposal of newborns was commonly accepted in ancient Greece, particularly those with physical abnormalities. In *Historia Animalium*, Aristotle wrote: 'As to exposing or rearing the children born, let there be a law that no deformed child shall be reared.' According to Plutarch's account of the Spartan state under Lycurgus, the elders examined all babies born to see if they were healthy enough to rear. If the newborn was handicapped the elders ordered that it be sent to die at a place called Apothetae, a ravine at the foot of Mount Taygetus.

In Rome, once the baby had been certified as fit, the next task for the midwife was the severing of the umbilical cord. Soranus warned that this should be undertaken using a knife, and disapproved strongly of any other method. Apparently, some midwives used pieces of glass, reeds, or thin crusts of hard bread, and he felt that these items could cause inflammation. From this it can be surmised that he saw a connection between dirt and infection. He also advised that the cord should not be cut immediately after birth, but that the infant should be left to rest for a short while. This practice has recently been adopted by some modern midwives, as blood still flows from the placenta to the baby for several minutes after birth, which is of great benefit to newborns, particularly those of low birth weight.

Interestingly, the placenta was of great importance in Pharaonic Egypt, and Tutankhamun's placenta was one of the royal standards, displayed on temple walls during royal processions. After birth, the mother and baby were washed in the river and the umbilical cord was kept in the house.

Once the cord had been cut and tied, the Roman midwife would wash the newborn and sprinkle it with a moderate amount of 'fine and powdery salt or natron or aphronitre'. These products are known to be mildly astringent and probably would have helped to remove the residue of vernix (the protective layer on a baby's skin in the womb) and amniotic fluid from the skin and also would have helped to prevent rashes. Soranus recommended a gentle rub of salt with honey, olive oil or the juice of barley, fenugreek or mallow onto the skin, which was to be washed away and then rubbed on again. A little olive oil would then be rubbed over the baby's eyes and a piece of wool soaked in olive oil put over the umbilical cord. Soranus warned against using cumin on the umbilicus as promoted by others, as he felt it was far too pungent for a vulnerable infant. He continually stressed that newborns were delicate and always suggested mild treatments that would cause no discomfort.

Although babies in Egypt were fortunate enough to be naked most of the time, in most other ancient societies babies were swaddled in cloths following their first bath. This practice was believed to avert the common complaint of rickets, a weakening of the bones caused by vitamin D deficiency, which was rife throughout the ages. Swaddling was thought to produce good, harmonious physical development.

Another reason for swaddling was to keep the baby warm. Tight wrappings ensured the baby could not throw off its coverings. Before swaddling, a little oil would be rubbed into the baby's bottom to prevent nappy rash. Soranus advised 'anointing the body with Etruscan wax melted together with olive oil before swaddling. This softens and warms the body and nourishes and whitens it'. Wrapping would then begin, and towards the end a small mattress would be included in the package, making it unbendable. It must have been extremely hot for these babies during the summer months, and this, coupled with having wet cloth rubbing against their skin often caused babies to be covered in skin rashes. Swaddled newborns were sometimes hung on the wall to keep them out of harm's way, particularly if animals were around. Unfortunately it was not uncommon for infants to suffocate due to the tight swaddling bands and their 'crucified' position.

Galen wrote of the newborn as a sort of sponge, wet, soft and malleable, in need of formation by its nurse. In Greece and Rome it was thought that a baby should be moulded into an adult shape. Plato wrote in the fourth century BC that children, 'while still soft, shall be moulded like wax'. A baby's legs were thought to distort through too much pressure, and parents were advised to swaddle them for the first two or three months following birth, then gradually reduce the amount of swaddling, 'when the body has become reasonably firm and there is no longer fear of any of its parts being distorted'. This gradual release from swaddling followed the Hippocratic reasoning of protecting a newborn as fully as possible from sudden changes, minimising the shock of birth and protectively guiding the infant physically into its new and hostile environment. Unfortunately, swaddling probably encouraged rather than prevented distorted bones.

In Rome a daily bath was recommended for babies. They would be unswaddled, bathed, massaged and reswaddled again. Soranus also advocated the benefits of gentle manual bending and stretching 'to massage and model every part so that imperceptibly that which is not yet fully formed is shaped into its natural characteristics'. Some doctors recommended a number of 'strong and sudden' techniques for firming a newborn's limbs, including immersing them in cold water and tying them inside a hollow log. Soranus denounced these methods, stating they were, 'hard to endure and cruel'. Despite his evident concern for babies, Soranus did offer some dubious advice on caring for newborns. He recommended that the infant should be dangled upside down by the feet while naked, 'in order that the vertebrae may be separated, the spine given the right curves and the sinews be untangled'.

The Suckling Infant
In early cultures infant mortality was high. Survival of the fittest ensured that usually only those babies nursed by their mothers

survived. There is evidence that hand-feeding was attempted, as feeding vessels have been discovered in infant graves. It is evident from ancient art that milk from domestic animals such as donkeys, camels and goats was often used as a substitute for mother's milk. Sometimes the baby would be held under the animal to feed directly from it.

Attempts to hand-feed babies in the days before sterilisation was discovered were doomed to failure because feeding equipment would have been impossible to keep clean. Until rubber teats were invented it was difficult to solve the problem of how to get the milk from the vessel into the baby's mouth. Feeding vessels were made of pottery and had awkward corners that were a breeding ground for bacteria. Teats were made using all sorts of items including linen, sponges, and pickled cows' teats. No adequate substitute for the mother's nipple could be found.

In his medical manuscript *De re medicina*, believed to date to around AD 30, Aulus Cornelius Celsus of Rome wrote that diarrhoea 'carries off mostly children up to the age of ten', which indicates that the high infant mortality rate was perhaps due to hand-feeding. If a mother was unable to feed her own baby, perhaps if she was too weak following the birth or if she found the whole notion repulsive, then a safer alternative to hand-feeding was the hiring of a wet nurse. There is evidence that wet-nursing was popular in ancient times: the Bible records that the Pharaoh's daughter called upon a Hebrew mother to nurse baby Moses, assuring her that she would receive payment. In Egyptian harems in the second century AD women frequently nursed each other's babies, and in Rome wet-nursing was an organised business. Nearly all early documents relating to infant feeding offer a good deal of advice to mothers on what to look out for when hiring a wet nurse: their milk was to be scrutinised and the colour and taste checked to make sure it was not poisonous.

Nineteenth-century sketch by Sir Edward Coley Burne-Jones
showing the Old Testament story of the finding of Moses

Mothers were advised to encourage the wet nurse to eat only food resembling the character of the desirable infant she was 'creating', such as eggs and wheat bread, because they were 'soft and most agreeable'. Celery, mint, and beans were all thought to contaminate the milk and were to be avoided, and sexual relations were also forbidden for wet nurses.

Soranus discouraged women from breast-feeding for at least three weeks after birth, believing that the mother's body, 'is in a bad state, agitated and changed [...] dried up, toneless, discoloured and in the majority of cases feverish as well [...] it is absurd to prescribe the maternal milk until the body enjoys stable health'.

While the ancient Egyptians appreciated the benefits of breast milk and breast-fed their babies until they were about three years old, Musonius Rufus, a contemporary of Soranus, considered it beneficial to starve a newborn for the first two days following birth:

> If you wish that the infant shoot up properly in accordance with nature, don't stuff it with food [...] the first food one ought to give an infant is honey, for it stimulates the tastebuds; further, it purges the body and the intestines [...] Infants who present the most ideal condition for nutrition are those born thin, those whose skin allows increasing volume; on the other hand those who have much fleshiness at birth do not have solid flesh, but actually thin out as they grow. The first, that is to say, the thin infants, need to gain, while the chubby infants need evacuation.

Since lactation works on a supply and demand basis it must have been difficult to establish breast-feeding so long after the birth. However babies were fed, it was seen as crucial to 'mould' them into good characters from the moment they were born so that they would become respectable members of Roman society. Responsibility for this was placed on the mother or wet nurse, as it was assumed that character and moral values could be transferred via the breast milk.

The physician Oribasius, writing in the fourth century AD believed:

> It is necessary to show now how one conserves health in an individual in whom nature is completely good. If a man constituted as well as possible is put under the care of a doctor practised in the art of conserving health, this is a happy man indeed; if he is placed under this care from the instant of his birth, in this way the soul also benefits, as a good regime produces good character [...] but now we ought to say how one recognises whether the newborn infant is well made, and following this, we show the regime for them.

Italian tinted engraving of the birth of the Virgin Mary

Some of the more brutal practices inflicted on children in classical times – infanticide, abandonment, and the sale of children – left an enduring legacy in Europe for centuries to come. Advice from Greek and Roman authors on the best ways to rear children carried such authority that it influenced generations born many hundreds of years later.

It is easy to assume that parents in the classical world were indifferent to their children, but there is evidence to suggest that close and loving relationships existed between them. A first century AD child's sarcophagus displayed in the Museo Nazionale at Agrigento in Sicily depicts the child's bereft parents and grandparents grieving over their loss. It was, however, the rise of Christianity across Europe that led to an improvement in the status of children as a new Christian morality began to take hold across the continent.

2

HOLY MAIDENHOOD:

– MOTHERHOOD IN THE MIDDLE AGES –

AFTER THE FALL of the last Western Roman Emperor in the fifth century AD, the Christian Church gradually assumed power for itself, using religion to impose order on society. Clergymen dedicated their lives to chastity and made little effort to disguise their disapproval of the 'weaker' sex, and the Church was the greatest preserver of male superiority. Saint Jerome, a leading early theologian, condemned women, using the book of Ecclesiastes in the Bible to justify his opinions: 'I found one upright man among a thousand, but not one upright woman amongst them all.' Ironically, according to the New Testament, Jesus taught that men and women were spiritually equal.

The Church discouraged women from becoming too involved with spiritual responsibilities. After all, the story of Eve clearly demonstrated that women were not to be trusted. The doctrine of original sin taught that every baby born carried the weight of the first sin ever committed by Adam and Eve. As Eve was responsible for tempting Adam into eating the fruit from the Tree of Knowledge, every descendent of Eve, and therefore every woman alive, was regarded as dangerous. During the fourth and fifth centuries AD even marriage was not considered a decent way of containing the dangerous influence of women, and virginity was promoted as the ideal state for both sexes.

The Virgin Mary was exalted, yet ordinary women were regarded as the epitome of imperfection. The early Church followed Hebrew law concerning the impurity of women and feared menstruating women as the Greeks and Romans had. This fear was passed down through the generations, continuing negative attitudes towards women. Those in the early Church thought it wise to protect themselves against possible demonic contamination from women by following rules that kept women at a safe distance. Women were only allowed to take Holy Communion from under a veil and were not allowed near sacred objects. Church leaders also described the horrendous monsters that would be born if a couple had intercourse during menstruation.

A Wife in Subjugation

Many women took to the convents during the Middle Ages as a way of avoiding life with a husband and the perpetual cycle of pregnancy. Those who married were seen merely as hosts nursing a child in their womb. They had no rights and were given little respect. If a woman gave birth to a mentally handicapped child her husband was within his rights to beat her.

Despite this, however, there were many women who assumed a dominant role in the household, shouldering responsibility and running businesses in the absence of their husbands; it is estimated that at least 10 per cent of medieval English households were run by widows.

Marriage continued to be constrained by the Church, with strict rules imposed on the act of intercourse. Although religious men decreed that sex during marriage was acceptable if the object was the production of children rather than the satisfaction of lustful feelings, they could not tolerate the idea that parishioners indulged themselves carnally whenever they felt like it. The Church therefore only permitted married couples to have intercourse on certain days of the year. It was not sex itself that proved so worrying to the clergy, but the lust that accompanied it. According to Peter Lombard, a twelfth-century theologian:

> If the first humans had not sinned there would have been carnal union in Paradise without any sin or stain and there would have been an 'undefiled bed' (Hebrews 13:4) there and union without concupiscence. Furthermore, they would have commanded the genital organs like other organs, so they would not have felt any unlawful movement there. Just as we move some bodily members towards others, such as the hand to the mouth, without the ardour of lust, likewise they would have used the genital organs without any itching of the flesh.

Before the Fall in the Garden of Eden Adam and Eve would have had intercourse to comply with God's order to 'increase and multiply', but would have done so merely with this aim in mind and without any intention of enjoying the act.

Men of the cloth found it difficult to tolerate the possibility that anyone would take pleasure in sexual activity but found the notion of female lust particularly disturbing. A woman was expected to involve herself in matters of the flesh solely to fulfil her wifely duties, not in reaction to personal desires.

Concern about this matter was reflected in contemporary literature such as *The Canterbury Tales* by Geoffrey Chaucer. The parson remarks that his wife 'has the merit of chastity who yields the debt of the body to her husband, yes, though it be contrary to her liking and the desire of her heart'.

From the middle of the thirteenth century the Church became more lenient towards women, and efforts were made to promote the marital state as a desirable option. The Church taught that childbirth was the best way to rid a woman of the original sin inherited from Eve, and sexual intercourse could only be justified if occurring within marriage. The First Letter of Paul to the Corinthians was often quoted:

> It is good for a man not to touch a woman. Nevertheless, to avoid fornication, let every man have his own wife, and let every woman have her own husband. Let the husband render unto the wife due benevolence: and likewise also the wife unto the husband. The wife hath not power of her own body, but the husband: and likewise also the husband hath not power of his own body, but the wife.

If the marriage debt was not met and either partner issued a complaint, the matter would be investigated in a bedroom trial. In such cases a group of wise matrons would be gathered to either test a woman's virginity or a man's genitals. Although rare, a number of cases were reported. In early-fifteenth-century York a failing husband was subjected to a trial in which:

> The [...] witness exposed her naked breasts and with her hands warmed at the said fire, she held and rubbed the penis and testicles of the said John. And she embraced and frequently kissed the said John, and stirred him up in so far as she could to show his virility and potency, admonishing him for shame that he should then and there prove and render himself a man. And she says, examined and diligently questioned, that the whole time aforesaid, the said penis was scarcely three inches long [...] remaining without any increase or decrease.

Avoiding Pregnancy

The use of birth control was widespread throughout the classical world, but unfortunately the art was lost over time. As the centuries progressed women once again spent a considerable part of their lives either pregnant or breast-feeding. Contraceptives such as the sponge barrier method used at the time of Christ fell into disuse. As Christianity spread across Europe the limiting of fertility became taboo, and consequently methods of birth control were not discussed or passed down the generations as before.

Although the general use of contraception was limited, several books written in the twelfth century include some enlightening details of intercourse and the issues surrounding it. According to *Aliquando*, a famous theological text concerning contraception of the mid-twelfth century, pregnancy could be avoided by procuring 'poisons of sterility'. *Adulterii malum*, a canon on adultery by the Benedictine monk Gratian from the same period, describes intercourse conducted merely for pleasure as unacceptable, since it was not granted by God for this purpose. The text is assumed to be referring to *coitus interruptus*, as no artificial means of avoiding pregnancy are mentioned.

Another twelfth-century text, *Solet Quaeri* by Peter Lombard, debates whether those who marry for desire rather than for the intention of producing offspring are actually married. If a couple marry for desire but 'have not avoided generation of off-spring' they would be able to consider themselves truly married. It is clear that contraception was considered an abomination, as later it is stated that a couple are not married, 'either if they do not wish children to be born or also if by some evil act they bring it about that children are not born'. If offspring were avoided then a marriage was nullified.

It appears that many authors from this time were greatly concerned about the 'spilling of seed', and one of the first questions asked when a couple decided to marry was whether they intended to have children. In St Antoninus's *Confessionale III*, it is stated that it was a mortal sin to conduct the sexual act when outside the appropriate receptacle, 'in such a fashion that seed is not received in order to avoid offspring and generation'.

The texts *Aliquando* and *Adulterii Malum* were referred to by William of Pagula in the fourteenth century when he wrote to parish priests advising them to teach their parishioners that they should not attempt to avoid conception when knowing a woman carnally. He concluded that:

> It is necessary to make this public in church; for the penitentiaries of bishops know well that there are many these days who believe that the sin against nature in many cases is not a sin, which is a matter for grief. So the parish priest can safely say among his parishioners, 'You ought to know that if someone has knowingly and wilfully emitted the seed of coitus in any way other than naturally with his wife, he sins gravely.'

William of Pagula wrote about the sin of any unnatural spilling of a man's seed as a sin against nature, but it appears that *coitus interruptus* was considered particularly sinful. He mentioned that Judah's son Onan was struck down because, 'when knowing his wife he deprived her of conception by spilling his seed on the ground', and hence, 'those who labour in this vice and form of homicide are, spiritually, the enemies of God and the human race. For in what they do they are saying to God, "You created man and woman in order for them to multiply. We will devote care in order for them to grow less".'

Although *coitus interruptus* has undoubtedly been used by many since ancient times, its practice was condemned by the Church. The Genesis account of Onan was used to justify the Church's teaching that sex was only to be used in order to fill the earth with children: 'when he went in unto his brother's wife, that he spilled it on the ground, lest that he should give seed to his brother. And the thing which he did displeased the Lord: wherefore he slew him also.'

In late-twelfth-century Paris, Peter the Chanter, a noted theologian, discussed the ethics involved in procuring sterility and quoted the case of a woman who has been ruptured in the navel through repeated childbirth. The doctors tell her that if she gives birth again she will die. Nevertheless her husband asks for her rendering of the debt (sex). Is she bound to render it, since for certain she knows that she will die if she conceives? She knows that if she renders the debt she will conceive, because she is still young. Item, one asks if she can procure sterility for herself, not principally in order to impede childbirth, but in order not to die in childbirth.

So little value was placed on the lives of women that contraception was not considered acceptable even though its use would have saved many young women's lives. It is difficult to believe that any loving husband would have insisted on conjugal rights knowing that the ultimate price would be the death of his wife. Ironically, in a society where the use of contraception was frowned upon, abortion and infanticide were widely practised.

Abortion and Infanticide
Until recently the termination of a pregnancy meant considerable danger for women, yet often they were willing to risk pain and even death in order to achieve their aims, despite facing strong religious opposition. Achieving a termination would at least offer temporary reprieve from the debilitating cycle of constant childbearing, even if it did mean burning in the eternal fires of Hell upon their death.

One of the most widely used and effective methods of abortion was massage. Performed correctly it offered a high success rate. There were many other recommended techniques for abortion, such as those recorded by Avicenna of Persia in the eleventh century :

Abortion may be produced, by those who abhor pregnancy, by prolonged baths and increased respiratory effort. The fetus is deprived of fresh air, and consequently dies. Abortion may also be induced by drugs, fasting, purgation, excessive coitus and massaging of cervical os [bone].

St Antoninus regarded it a mortal sin for a mother to procure abortion, but he laid the blame on those who helped women to achieve their aims, such as doctors and apothecaries. He wrote that apothecaries should be questioned as to whether they dispensed drugs for the purpose of abortion and doctors should be asked if they 'give medicine to a pregnant woman to kill the fetus, even [...] for the preservation of the mother'.

Medieval Potion for Abortion

2 drachms of galbanum [gum resin] dissolved in goat's milk, so that the woman can easily take 2 or 3 ounces of the milk. [Or] make a suppository thus: take 2 drachms each of black olive oil, stavesacre [larkspur], round birthwort, rosemary, marjoram, the seeds of laurel, the succulent part of colocynth, the jum ammoniac, and 1 drachm of bull's fall: reduce to powder, with the exception of the aromatic resin, dissolve the juice of artemesia, then mix with it all the other ingredients and make a suppository.

– Avicenna of Persia, eleventh century AD

Some women, after failing to abort the fetus, had to continue the pregnancy in misery. Besides the physical toil involved they had to endure the emotional torment of carrying a child knowing throughout that they may be unable to support the baby once born. As during ancient times, the practice of exposing newborn infants was widespread in England during the Middle Ages, with female infants more commonly exposed than males. It is believed that the large dowries that fathers had to pay for their daughter to find a husband was part of the reason why so many baby girls were abandoned. The burden of a daughter was often too much for a family to bear.

Pope Gregory IX's *Decretales* featured three different texts concerning infant death, two of which were wilful killings. The first was a letter from Pope Alexander III to the Bishop of Tournai in which he wrote of an unmarried woman who killed her child. It was felt that she should stay in a convent for the rest of her life to do penance, although if she were found to be 'carnally fragile', and therefore unable to commit to a life without sexual fulfilment, she could be allowed to marry. The second was a letter from Pope Lucius III to the Bishop of Paris and concerned a married woman who wilfully killed her child. She also had other children and was not to be separated from them or her husband in order that they would still be cared for. The third was another letter from Pope Alexander III in which he wrote of the difficulties of deciding whether the death of an infant was accidental or not. He mentioned cases where infants 'are found dead with the father and mother, where it is not clear whether the baby was smothered or suffocated by the father or mother, or whether it died by its own death'.

St Antoninus's *Confessionale*, which contained questions to be asked by the priest during confession, listed abortions and infanticides of various motives:

If a pregnant woman has procured an abortion for herself through medicines or exertions or some other way.

If a woman kills her child wilfully in order to hide her crime [the crime of becoming pregnant out of wedlock].

If a mother or nurse stifles a child whom she is keeping beside her in a bed, inadvertently smothering her.

If a pregnant woman brings about an abortion which is contrary to her intention or plan, if she was committing obvious negligence in this, such as jumping too much, or working too much and inordinately, or through sexual activity in order to satisfy inordinate lust.

Some manuals discussed the problems of infanticide and exposure and ways to reduce the occurrence of infant death. In the monk Gratian's *Decretum*, compiled around 1140, outlines of infant care were given, and advice such as, 'Parents are to be admonished and publicly advised that they should not place beside themselves in a bed their babies, so that they should not be suffocated or smothered through some negligence which might arise; in this case they are guilty of homicide.'

Although rare, a few texts from the twelfth century promoted concern for the mother and contained suggestions for the prevention of infant death. The writer Robert of Flamborough suggested less penance on a 'little poor woman' who may have been driven to committing infanticide through numerous difficult circumstances, such as 'the difficulty of feeding the baby'. He described some circumstances where negligence rather than intent could cause the death of an infant, including 'If a mother had placed a baby on a hearth, and some man has put water in the cauldron, and the baby dies because of an overflow of boiling water'.

Peter the Chanter also dealt with the question of blame in various circumstances of abortion and exposure. A possible cause of abortion was mentioned where, 'A priest is following the hounds and smashes a pregnant woman against a wall. She falls down wailing. Afterwards for three weeks she is at home, complaining a bit; meanwhile, she goes on carrying things to the market. However, at the end of three weeks she has an abortion'. Peter questioned whether the priest was guilty. Another instance was given relating to a 'certain monk whose abbot had placed him in charge of a certain house. He finds outside the house which had been entrusted to him an abandoned little baby, very recently born, and already about to die through hunger and cold. The aforesaid monk wants to take him up and look after him. The brothers forbid him, and also the abbot, for two reasons: to avoid evil suspicion [...] and to avoid other little women being encouraged by this example to abandon their children in the same place, were they to see the brothers taking care of this baby'. Peter the Chanter stated that if the monk were to be disobedient and take the baby in, then his pity would be enough to excuse his disobedience.

Thomas of Chobham, the sub-deacon of Salisbury Cathedral, discussed various cases of abortion and infanticide in his thirteenth-century text *Summa Confessorum*, including exposure and denial of breast-feeding. He mentioned the case of a certain woman who 'wanted to cast out her fetus [...] she gave three jumps from a bench to the ground, and on the third jump the fetus fell out to the ground, wrapped round in a little skin. It is clear from this that the women who have not been instructed about this often eject some conceived fetus, either through work or exertion.'

Pregnancy

During the Middle Ages antenatal care was virtually unheard of. Pregnant women were fortunately exempt from fasting, a common act of devotion to God at the time, and anyone beating a pregnant woman was subject to ecclesiastical punishment, offering her temporary protection. This was virtually the extent of her special care, although the monk Bald's tenth-century *Leechbook* recommends that pregnant women 'should eat nothing salty or sweet, or drink beer, or eat swine's flesh or anything fat, or drink to intoxication, or travel by road, or ride too much on horseback, lest the child be born before the proper time'. Women probably worked during pregnancy until a few days before labour and perhaps right up to birth as it was commonly thought that intense physical labour could ease the future delivery.

Women were often denied the opportunity to balance their diet adequately. Men, the main breadwinners and the heads of the household, were usually given not only the biggest share of food, but also the most nutritious. Women fed on the leftovers and were seldom better nourished than their livestock. It was therefore difficult for women to maintain good health, particularly during pregnancy. They would have been unable to fight infections easily and were physically exhausted when bearing a child.

The cycle of pregnancy and breast-feeding coupled with inadequate diet often resulted in the early deaths of mother and child. Many women never lived to experience the menopause. Innumerable babies died before or soon after birth as a result of undernourishment in the womb.

> They sholde not speke afore a woman [...] grete with chylde of ony maner of mete that for the present and at a nede may not be founde, to the ende that the fruyte that she bereth haue not a marke upon his body.
>
> – *Gospelles of Dystaues* Part I, XVII, 1507

As a result of high maternal and infant mortality rates, many women paid great attention to the rituals and superstitions passed down through the generations. There were many situations to avoid during pregnancy if a healthy child were to be born, and therefore numerous constraints were imposed. It was believed that if a pregnant woman was startled by a dog her baby would be born with dog feet; a lunatic or sleepwalker would result if she looked at the moon.

Old Wives' Tales

If a pregnant woman sees a hare, the child will have a hare lip.

Pickled onions give birthmarks if eaten while pregnant.

Heartburn during pregnancy means the baby will have lots of hair.

Heartburn means a girl.

Take bicarbonate of soda to ensure a boy.

If the membranes rupture early, labour will be prolonged.

Do not stretch during pregnancy or the cord will go round the baby's neck.

If you see a snake while pregnant the baby will have green eyes.

Lose a tooth for every child you bear.

Tiptoe through the maydew and you will miscarry.

Sexual intercourse during pregnancy will make the child sensual.

If you long for sweet foods during pregnancy you will have a girl; if you long for sour things it will be a boy.

If you don't feel much movement during pregnancy it is a boy.

A lot of vomiting in pregnancy means an easy confinement.

Nausea early in pregnancy means it will be a girl.

Swing a wedding ring suspended on a cotton thread over the pregnant woman's stomach. If it goes in a circle it will be a girl; if it swings to and fro, it will be a boy.

Birth defects were considered to be the work of the Devil, and consequently women were desperate to do all they could to avoid them. Birthmarks were often known as the 'mark of Cain', originating from the Genesis story of Cain, son of Adam and Eve, who was branded with a permanent port wine stain on the skin of his face by God. He was eternally exiled for the murder of his brother, and therefore birthmarks were often interpreted as the mark of a criminal.

Ye sholde not gyve to yonge maydens to ete the heed of a hare [...] and in especyall to them that be wit chylde, for certaynly theyre chyldren might haue couen lyppes.

– *Gospelles of Dystaues*, Part I, VIII, 1507

Birthmarks were also thought to be one of the signs of a werewolf, as were stubby fingers and excess body hair, particularly in late Medieval and Renaissance Europe. Anyone suspected of lycanthropy (being a werewolf) was persecuted. Many young men were actually executed after being suspected as werewolves, although surprisingly all remained in their human form despite their extenuating circumstances! It is understandable then that mothers ran themselves ragged while pregnant trying to avoid the unavoidable. A pregnant woman during medieval times may have become upset any time she had to leave the house as hairy men or those with birthmarks would have been difficult to avoid and if she laid eyes upon either she would have feared for the health of her baby. She would then no doubt be condemned as hysterical and blamed for causing emotional harm to her unborn child.

Women in Medicine

Through most of the Middle Ages obstetrical literature was limited to translated work from the Greeks and Romans, but gradually new manuscripts began to appear, reaffirming a woman's right to be cared for by a woman, such as the *Medieval Women's Guide to Health*:

> And although women have various maladies and more terrible sicknesses than any man knows, as I said, they are ashamed for fear of reproof in time to come and of exposure by discourteous men who love women only for physical pleasure and for evil gratification. And if women are sick such men despise them and fail to realise how much sickness women have before they bring them into the world. And so, to assist women, I intend to write of how to help their secret maladies so that one woman may aid another in her illness and not divulge her secrets to such discourteous men.

For much of history women have cared for the sick and provided healthcare for the needy in society. Wise women gathered herbs and made them into remedies to help relieve all manner of symptoms, including the pain associated with childbirth. Despite this, men's names predominate in the history of medicine. Part of the reason is that many women were illiterate, had no access to education and were forbidden from attending medical school, and consequently most of the surviving historical manuscripts were written by men. One of the most well-known female practitioners from the twelfth century was the writer, composer and mystic Hildegard of Bingen, author of two medical manuscripts and an authority on herbal medicines.

Another physician who gained respect in the area of general medicine and obstetrics during the eleventh century was Trotula of Salerno. She was considered an expert midwife who advised doctors on how to deal with the complications of childbirth. She is often associated with the legendary old Dame Trot, and apparently Chaucer based the midwife from *The Canterbury Tales* on her character. In her text, now known as the *Medieval Women's Guide to Health,* Trotula of Salerno claimed that physical defects in both men and women could affect conception; a bold claim indeed to suggest that males could be the cause of infertility. She also prescribed opiates for the pain of childbirth, going against the Christian belief that women should suffer during labour as a punishment from God for Eve's sin.

Throughout the Middle Ages the majority of women in Europe were attended to by midwives during labour. The position of the midwife remained secure due to the many taboos concerning childbirth and the female body, and men were happy to leave well alone. The word 'midwife' literally means 'with-wife'. Their skills were passed down through the generations and their experience was practical rather than theoretical. Their knowledge of the female reproductive system was far greater than that of the physician.

The techniques used remained similar to those employed in ancient times, such as tying a cloth around a labouring woman's abdomen and tightening it with each contraction to help push the baby out.

Although the Church imposed strict rules on the role of medicine, it did provide society with a valuable asset: from the seventh century onwards the Church in England opened hospitals organised by nuns. Christians taught that it was the duty of everyone to ensure that the poor, sick and homeless were cared for. The earliest hospitals began as guesthouses for pilgrims but gradually grander buildings were specially built for the purpose. Some of these hospitals remain operational today, such as St Bartholomew's and St Thomas's hospitals in London, founded in the twelfth and thirteenth centuries respectively. Beds were provided in some of these medieval hospitals for women in labour.

Complications of pregnancy were usually dealt with efficiently and calmly. Midwives were easily able to deal with births where the umbilical cord was looped around the baby's neck and were often able to perform version, the ancient technique of turning a malpresented baby. They would only intervene in the birth process when absolutely necessary and avoided putting their hands inside a labouring woman if at all possible as it was thought that interference of this kind could stop contractions.

Towards the end of the Middle Ages there were signs that medicine was emerging from the torpor into which it had slumped. There was a new intellectual freedom from the constraints of the Church, and the beginnings of some organised medical training for midwives began to emerge in the shape of new midwifery schools both in England and abroad.

The Grim Reality of Birth

For women in bygone years the birth of a baby was full of danger for both mother and child. Complications such as breech births were dreaded, and birth defects and even death were very real possibilities for both mother and child. Even in the absence of any complications women knew that they would experience intense pain with no available relief.

Birth almost always took place in the home, usually in a small room separate from the main living area, which would have been kept free from draughts. Peasant women who were unable to enjoy the luxury of a choice of room had to deliver their baby in the main living area, on the bare floor or on sacks of hay. One thing they were able to rely on was the support of their female friends and relations, and sometimes as many as thirty people would surround the labouring woman, offering advice and encouragement.

In most instances a midwife, sometimes accompanied by assistants, would attend to the labouring woman, since the birthing chamber was almost always exclusively the province of women. Male physicians were only called in emergencies when surgery was necessary.

A fire was often lit during labour, and the temperature in the birthing chamber must have risen again due to the presence of so many bodies. Heat was seen as beneficial to the labouring woman and to the infant and was also needed to heat water for bathing after birth. For those women from noble and wealthy families the birthing chamber was prepared carefully; floors were freshly swept, the best coverlets were placed on the beds and everything put in its proper place.

Women during medieval times continued to assume a sitting or squatting position for delivery. Positions favouring gravity were used if the woman was comfortable enough, and she would often support herself with a rope or sheet flung over the rafters.

During the fifteenth century the ancient idea of using a birthing stool to support a woman in the upright position during delivery was reintroduced in Italy and quickly became popular all over Europe. When unable to obtain the specially shaped horseshoe chair, a woman would sometimes rest her legs on two chairs placed alongside each other and balance in the middle, though this must have only been attempted by those with very strong thigh muscles! Those with a weaker constitution would sometimes sit on another woman's lap and deliver through her legs, as was popular in the classical world. The midwife would often rub the mother's abdomen in order to ease pain and hasten delivery of the infant.

Superstitions remained prevalent, and there were various unusual ideas on how a woman could make labour easier for herself or induce the birth. Women were sometimes whipped to induce labour, and sometimes watched others being whipped. According to one German myth, an Empress whose baby was overdue was taken into a room to observe twenty men being whipped, two of whom died. She was so horrified at what she had witnessed that she successfully went into labour.

The birth attendant would allow nothing to surround the labouring woman that could possibly impede or block delivery. All rings, laces, knots, fastenings and buckles had to be removed. Doors and windows were opened, bottles uncorked and sometimes horses set free. Crossing legs in front of a pregnant woman was viewed as a way of ensuring that she would have a difficult birth. If birth was delayed longer than twenty contractions members of the household might even fire arrows in the air, which were symbolic of the opening of the womb.

In order to combat pain during the birth a warm cloth was sometimes placed on the mother's abdomen but few other practical methods were used. Alcohol, opium and Indian hemp were often used when pain relief was needed for other medical problems, but were not usually given to a labouring woman. Pain was viewed as a necessary part of labour, a punishment from God for all women to bear since the time of Eve. Any relief from pain was still seen as denying God the satisfaction of hearing a woman's repentant screams.

A woman experiencing great travail during labour would try to draw strength from the good intentions of the caring attendants surrounding her. Well-meaning attendants would offer her various items thought to ease delivery. Certain stones were often used as amulets, and jasper was seen as particularly helpful in encouraging a safe delivery. Hildegard of Bingen recommended that a pregnant woman should carry a jasper in her hand throughout her pregnancy and during the birth in order to spurn the Devil, since childbirth was considered fertile ground for supernatural forces.

If the birth proved difficult and complications arose, for example, when a baby presented in a difficult position for birth, certain instruments were used. The least horrifying of these was a blunt hook, used to pull on the baby's legs in a breech delivery. Other instruments that struck fear into women were sharp hooks, called crochets, and knives. While probably saving the mother's life, they would literally pull the baby out piece by piece. Most surgical procedures were carried out by barber-surgeons, although midwives during the Middle Ages, particularly those in urban areas, almost always carried an iron hook with them. Before using the hook they were supposed to call for help from other midwives to ensure that the baby was dead, then proceed to extract it. For a mother suffering the agonies of prolonged labour, the sight of her midwife wielding a sharp hook must have been truly terrifying.

Primitive knife used for Caesarean section

If a mother managed to deliver her baby vaginally there was the possibility of a ruptured perineum (tearing between the vagina and anus). A description of how to repair a ruptured perineum was included in Trotula of Salerno's *Medieval Women's Guide to Health*, one of the earliest medical treatises written in the vernacular. After washing the area with wine and butter, the midwife was advised to 'sew up the breach [...] in three or four places with a double silken thread. Then put a linen cloth into the part, that is to say the vulva, according to its size. And afterward cover it with hot tar, and that will make the womb withdraw and thus remain firm because of the evil smell of the tar, and then the breach will be healed and closed with powder of comfrey, little daisy and cinnamon'.

There are records of attempted Caesarean sections when mothers were unable to continue to push the baby out due to exhaustion or if the baby was stuck in an awkward position. Throughout the Middle Ages there was no improvement in surgical techniques and reports of Caesareans almost always ended tragically. Although it was known that a woman would probably not survive such an operation, it remained an important procedure as it meant that mother and child could be buried separately. It is not clear how many women survived the operation though some successful cases were documented. One such story involved Jacob Nufer, a Swiss pig gelder whose wife experienced complications during birth in 1500. He called in thirteen local midwives and two local surgeons, who were all unable to help her. In desperation he performed a Caesarean operation on her himself and both mother and child survived, she to bear him several more children.

There may have been other unrecorded successes in earlier centuries but they would certainly have been few and far between. To perform a Caesarean it is necessary to first cut through the abdomen, the connective tissues between the major muscles and the fatty layer, then the bladder has to be lifted and placed aside in order to cut through the wall of the uterus. Caesareans were usually only performed on dead mothers. The shock of this operation on a woman who had not been anaesthetised would almost certainly have been too much for her body to bear. If she survived this she may have died from infection or internal bleeding.

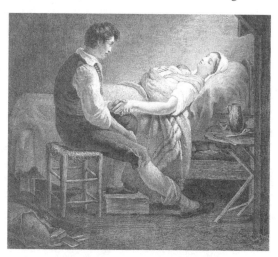

Nineteenth-century illustration of an
exhausted new mother clasping her child

Wrapped in Swaddling Clothes

Once a baby was born into a medieval family it would have been bathed by the midwife in warm water which was ready prepared on the fire in the birthing chamber. In wealthy homes milk or wine was sometimes used instead of water. Trotula of Salerno recommended that a newborn's tongue should be washed with hot water to ensure that the child would be able to speak properly. Honey was sometimes used to rub on the tongue in order to promote a healthy appetite.

Once bathed, the infant would be swaddled in linen strips so that its limbs would grow straight, then laid in a crib in a dark corner of the room.

It has always been considered beneficial to a newborn to recreate the conditions of the womb in order to promote a feeling of security. It was thought best to continue the darkness of the womb

Medieval illuminated manuscript showing babies carried in baskets

and was in keeping with the words of Psalm 121: 'The sun shall not smite thee by day, nor the moon by night', a scripture often read at the 'churching' of women, a ceremony to 'cleanse' them after childbirth. It was recommended that the mother should also remain in the same dark room for quiet rest and recovery. The midwife would serve her drinks and broths to speed her recovery and offer dressings and ointments to quell her bleeding and ease the discomfort of inflammation.

It was thought that a baby cried when born because it realised what its new world was like. This early-fifteenth-century poem is the earliest surviving lullaby:

> Lollay, lollay, littel child, why wepestow so sore?
> Nedes mestow wepe, hit was iyarked thee yore
> Ever to lib in sorrow, and sich and mourn therefore,
> As thyn eldren did ere this, whil hi alives wore.
> Lollay, lollay, littel child, child, lollay, lullow,
> Into uncuth world ycomen so ertow.
>
> Child, thou ert a pilfrim in wickedness yborn;
> Thou wandrest in this fals world – thou loke thee beforn!
> Deth shall come with a blast ute of a well dim horn
> Adames kin down to cast, himsilp hath ydo beforn.
> Lollay, lollay, little child, so wo thee worth Adam
> In the lond of Paradis throgh wickedness of Satan.

With so many female friends and relatives around, women were able to rest following birth. The mother was able to focus all her attention on the newborn baby while the household chores were taken care of by others. Various methods were employed to comfort a fretful infant such as massage and bathing. Mothers would also often rock their infant in their arms and sing soothing lullabies. Rockers, women who were employed for the sole purpose of rocking the baby, often worked in shifts due to the long hours demanded of them.

> Lully, lulley, lulley, lulley,
> The faucon [falcon] hath born my mak [mate] away.
> He bare him up, he bare him down,
> He bare him into an orchard brown.
> Lully, lulley, lulley, lulley,
> The faucon hath born my mak away.
> — Medieval Corpus Christi Carol

Rocking must have been especially enjoyable for a swaddled baby who would have been unable to move any other way. Many babies suffered extreme discomfort, wrapped tightly in a cocoon-like parcel. Sore, itchy, caked in excrement and unable to wriggle, stretch or even suck its own thumb, a soothing rocking motion must have been the only way to surrender itself into blessed oblivion. Sometimes a swinging box was hung between two posts to rock the child. An example of this sort of cradle can be seen in the Museum of London. Later forms were boxes on rockers with hoods over the head end to protect the baby from bright light and draughts.

> As soon as the child is born it must be swathed; lay it to sleep in its cradle, and you must have a nurse to rock it to sleep.
> — Walter de Biblesworth, late thirteenth century

Purification of New Mothers

Women were seen as even more spiritually unclean after childbirth, suffering exclusion from the Church just when they most needed support. The medieval Church followed the Hebrew law forbidding women from entering a holy place for thirty-three days after the birth of a son and sixty-six days after the birth of a daughter. Women then had to attend a churching ceremony, which would reintegrate them into the congregation.

Prayer books from the eleventh century contained a special service for this purification, although such customs existed much earlier than this. In ancient Israel, for example, a new mother was expected to attend the temple with offerings to atone for her sins. The New Testament reiterated the importance of purification by recording the attendance of Mary at the temple with her newborn son, and Hippolytus, an early Christian theologian, wrote that a newly delivered mother should sit among the catechumens (unbaptised persons undergoing instruction). Despite the widespread agreement that women were impure following the birth of a child, not all religious leaders advocated this view. As related in Bede's *Ecclesiastical History of England*, Augustine of Canterbury, founder of the Christian Church in southern England, wrote to Pope Gregory the Great asking how soon a new mother could come into the church. Pope Gregory advised that even if the mother entered the church an hour after giving birth she would not be committing a sin, and forbidding her to come would turn the punishment she was bearing for Eve into a crime. His advice was not followed, however; many churchmen felt safer if the evil temptresses known as women were kept at bay.

During the Middle Ages women were still led to believe that childbirth offered the best means of escaping from original sin. In *Hali Meidenhad* (Holy Maidenhood), a thirteenth-century manuscript concerning virginity, the author described the struggle involved in bearing children: 'Thy ruddy face shall turn lean and grow green as grass. Thine eyes shall be dusky and underneath grow pale; And by the giddiness of thy brain thy head shall ache sorely.'

There was little advance in the scientific understanding of how a woman's body worked from Roman times. Galen had produced a mass of medical information, based on the dissections he had performed on animals. His descriptions of the anatomy of the human body were influenced by his belief that a divine creator had produced all the organs for a specific purpose. Since this view was particularly appealing to both Christians and Muslims, his work survived the intervening centuries well into the Middle Ages.

The dangers of childbirth remained high during the Middle Ages, and the death of the mother, child or both was always a strong possibility. Apart from a few herbal remedies, little effort was made in the field of medicine as it was felt that life was merely a short interlude before heavenly reward, and suffering was a means of salvation. Though there was great concern that babies should be baptised as soon as possible after birth, little regard was shown for the mother. Midwives were told that if they had to make a choice between the life of the mother or the baby, then they should choose the baby. If a woman died during childbirth or even during pregnancy, she would often be buried in unconsecrated ground, as it was feared her pollution might contaminate others.

Suckling

One of the most important ways a mother could protect her baby and ensure its good health was to breast-feed rather than hand-rear it; however, there were so many taboos associated with women's bodies that breast-feeding was often considered too repulsive to practise.

Some mothers claimed not to want to suckle their infants because, in addition to ruining their figures, it would prevent them from 'frolicking' with their husbands, due to the widely held view that semen soured breast milk. Since it was common for infants to be nursed until at least two or three years of age it is understandable that many husbands and wives became impatient.

A safer alternative to hand-feeding was to employ the services of a wet nurse. It was a particularly common practice among the aristocrats and merchant class of Europe, which may explain why the wealthy had more children than women in the lower classes, since lactation suppresses fertility. Some children who were sent away to live with their wet nurse were breast-fed until the age of two or three and then returned to their parents once weaned.

Mothers who did nurse their own infants were given much advice by men about how and when to breast-feed a baby as paediatric literature began to circulate amongst a much wider audience following the introduction of mass printing techniques to Europe in the fifteenth century.

Naming the Child

One of the first priorities following the birth of a baby was to arrange baptism, often within a week of the birth. Parents were instructed not to defer any longer than the Sunday or next holy day following the birth of their baby, an urgency that was of course a result of the high infant mortality rate. Medieval theologians developed the concept of limbo, a place where unbaptised infants went following death. Consequently parents were terrified of losing their child before it was baptised and assured a place in Heaven. They would have to suffer the agony of loss during their time on earth but could look forward to being reunited for eternity. If a baby died before being christened it was buried in the far north corner of a churchyard, a place normally reserved for suicides.

The ceremony of baptism ended the ambiguous period for the baby by forsaking the Devil and forming membership with Christ. This was seen not only as guaranteed spiritual security, but also as a defence against evil spirits that were believed to cause the death of a child. In the absence of any effective medical treatment parents had to arm themselves with the only protection against childhood illnesses available to them.

It was not necessary to be named in order to be baptised, but for the child to be registered in the church records and therefore recorded in the 'Book of Life' it was important for a name to be given. Only about twenty Christian names

Illustration from 1503 of a childbirth scene showing a new mother recovering in bed while the infant is bathed by an attendant

were used during the Middle Ages in all Western countries, with John and Mary being the most popular. In the early years of Christianity many people changed their first names, which were considered pagan, to Christian names in order to be baptised; hence the 'given' name became known as the Christian name.

Evidence shows that infanticide and the abandonment of children occurred throughout medieval Europe, but such practices were not necessarily indicative of lack of parental sentiment as much as the harsh realities of life at the time. The impact of Christianity had led to a higher status for young children than they had previously enjoyed, and close, loving relationships, particularly between mothers and their infants, were formed. However, in medieval times children as young as seven were expected to become part of adult society, and it wasn't until the nineteenth century that childhood as an entirely separate state came to be recognised.

3

BIRTH PANGS:

– MOTHERS IN TUDOR AND STUART ENGLAND –

> Let the woman learn in silence with all subjection. But I suffer not a woman to teach, nor to usurp authority over the man, but to be in silence. For Adam was first formed, then Eve. And Adam was not deceived, but the woman being deceived was in the transgression. Notwithstanding she shall be saved in childbearing, if they continue in faith and charity and holiness with sobriety.
>
> – 1 Timothy, 2:12–15

UNTIL RECENTLY IT was the prerogative of men to secure themselves an education and proceed to teach new generations the ways of the world. Women were forbidden to teach or even obtain an education. Lack of education and overpowering religious loyalty led to an unquestioning acceptance of their role and position in life. Widespread female illiteracy in Tudor and Stuart England means that there is a lack of records written by women, making it difficult to ascertain their feelings as members in a society with no rights or respect. Historical sources clearly show that although life was difficult for both sexes, the prejudices that existed and the false assumptions drawn from the Bible had dramatic consequences for women, particularly during their childbearing years.

During the sixteenth and seventeenth centuries the idea that the only contribution women could make to society was as

Dutch seventeenth-century illustration of a lying-in room with attendant, child being bathed and a midwife drinking beer

childbearers remained prevalent. Their physical and mental welfare was not considered important; only their essential role as guarantors of future offspring was valued. Despite the toll on their bodies and the risk of death or disability that arose with each labour, women entered marriage feeling that they must deliver as many children as possible. Barren women were considered blighted by God, even though these were the very women who were likely to live longest and enjoy much better health than their more fertile contemporaries. The very women who suffered from the associated problems of constant childbearing felt pity for their childless sisters.

During the sixteenth century a religious revolution took place which divided western Christians into two camps: Catholic and Protestant. The belief that the only justification for sex was the procreation of children continued during this period, and, as Puritan beliefs gained popularity, the emphasis on the literal interpretation of the Bible increased, particularly with relation to certain passages such as 'go forth and multiply and fill the earth'. Any barrier placed in the way of prolific childbearing was condemned by men of God as immoral.

With-child

Many taboos continued throughout society during the sixteenth and seventeenth centuries, and the connection between intercourse and pregnancy was not always appreciated by young couples. First pregnancies often came as a shock to newlyweds, and many a woman would not realise she was pregnant until a visible bump appeared.

For those who suspected they were carrying a child, there was no reliable way to verify it, and it could be months before a pregnancy was confirmed. Even then there could be difficulties, as in the case of Mary Tudor. She married at the age of thirty-eight and was convinced she was pregnant a few months after her wedding. Her physicians confirmed this, and she reported that she had felt the baby moving. She moved to Hampton Court to prepare for confinement. Daily prayers were said for her safe delivery but as each month passed it grew increasingly obvious that the Queen was not pregnant and never had been. Her humiliation was complete a few weeks later when her young husband, Philip of Spain, abandoned her.

The Queen may have experienced various signs that led her to believe she was pregnant, and these signs would have been her only guide. Women had to rely on noticing subtle changes in their bodies in order to detect a pregnancy; due to poor nutrition menstrual periods may have been irregular and therefore their absence would not necessarily have confirmed pregnancy. Clues to their condition included wan eyes, hard nipples, swollen veins, and clouded urine.

Further indications of a future addition to the family were luridly described in *Hali Meidenhad*:

> Your rosy face will grow thin, and turn green as grass; your eyes will grow dull, and shadowed underneath, and because of your dizziness your head will ache cruelly. Inside, in your belly, a swelling in your womb which bulges you out like a water-skin, discomfort in your bowels and stitches in your side, and often painful backache; heaviness in every limb; the dragging weight of your two breasts, and the streams of milk that run from them. Your beauty is all destroyed by pallor; there is a bitter taste in your mouth, and everything you eat makes you feel sick; and whatever food your stomach disdainfully receives – that is, with distaste – it throws up again.

Midwives could detect a pregnancy by internal examination, but by far the most definite signal for a woman would be the baby's stirrings, which occurred around the third or fourth month. It is surprising that the midwives employed to take care of Mary Tudor did not realise that the pregnancy was phantom, although it is possible that they did but were too frightened to break the news to her.

Once pregnant, a woman would take great care to avoid any unnecessary upset in order to maintain a healthy pregnancy. Superstitions regarding the development of the baby were widespread. Pregnant women were advised not to attend funerals in order to avoid harmful influences, and it was suggested that they refrain from intercourse for fear of strangling the baby. These concerns were deep-rooted, and most expectant mothers strictly adhered to the advice.

Pregnant women have always been advised to take extra-special care of themselves, both physically and emotionally. *The Expert Midwife* of 1637 advised: 'Let them take heed of cold and sharp winds, great heat, anger, perturbations of the mind, fears and terrors, immoderate Venus and all intemperance of eating and drinking.'

There was, however, very little practical help available for expectant mothers. Antenatal care was limited to the administration of herbs such as raspberry leaf tea (believed to promote an easy delivery), and regular bleeding sessions were considered vital in order to prevent the baby from drowning. This process entailed cutting into a vein with a sharp instrument in order to drain away 'excess blood'. Bleeding probably exacerbated anaemia, which often accompanies pregnancy, and no doubt left women feeling physically drained and exhausted. It was to be several hundred years before the dangerous complications of pregnancy such as eclampsia (convulsive fits in the last stages of pregnancy) were understood. Swelling around the wrists and ankles was often the first sign of eclampsia, which was usually ignored, but then fits would begin which often lasted for hours and ended in death.

What Will the Baby Be Like?
In the age before effective ante- and postnatal medical care, women approached labour with considerable trepidation, most acknowledging the possibility of death or disability both for themselves and the baby. Despite their very real fears, however, the birth of a new baby remained an exciting and cherished event. Just as parents today speculate as to what their baby will be like,

Pen and ink drawing from the sixteenth century showing a child receiving its first bath while the mother is in bed recovering and being given food

parents in the past tried to imagine their unborn baby in the womb, and once it was born they followed long-standing traditions in order to help establish the baby's developing character.

In an uncertain world it was comforting to ascertain the future, and many parents were anxious for a guide to their child's nature and prospects as soon as possible. Hence, in addition to godparents, astrologers often gathered in the birth chamber of a wealthy home. A horoscope could therefore be forecast at the moment of birth. Astrologers were often the only men allowed to be present at such an intimate occasion. For less fortunate families there were an abundance of folk rhymes that could foretell the child's future personality, such as 'Monday's Child', which is still well known today.

The timing of a child's entry into the world was considered to be of major significance, and it was widely thought that the moment of birth could have great influence on their future.

> The owl shriek'd at thy birth – an evil sign;
> The night-crow cried, aboding luckless time;
> Dogs howl'd, and hideous tempest shook down trees;
> The raven rook'd her on the chimney's top,
> And chattering pies in dismal discords sung.
> – William Shakespeare, *Henry VI*, 1590

May was thought to be an ill-omened month for birth as an old wives' tale said that 'a May baby's sickly – you may try but you'll never rear it'. Horses, cats and sows born during the witching month of May were all seen as unreliable. If, however, a baby was born on Christmas Day it was considered lucky, or, even better, Childermas Day on 28 December, which was certainly the best day of the year. The later in the day a child was born the shorter the life they would have. If a baby was born between midnight on Friday and dawn on Saturday it was thought that he or she would be favoured with second sight. Birth on the Sabbath was generally thought to signify good health and happiness, although the Puritans sometimes refused to baptise a child born on this day as they surmised that he or she must have been conceived on a Sunday!

Boy or Girl?

Those interested in guessing the sex of the child could follow the Hippocratic humoral system of diagnosis to guess the child's sex. When the four 'humours' – blood, yellow bile, black bile and phlegm – were out of equilibrium in the body, illness was thought to result. The humours correlated to various qualities: hot, dry, hard, thick, dexter (right-handed), ruddy and ascending indicated masculinity, while cool, moist, soft, slender, sinister (left-handed), pale and descending represented the female. The brightness of the woman's right eye, the swelling of her right breast, and the blush of her right cheek were all hopeful indications of a male. Doctors during the seventeenth century often repeated these indications, but admitted it was impossible to state for certain whether the baby would be a boy or girl. Astrologers claimed that the sex of the child depended on the configuration of the heavens at the moment of conception, and some parents were convinced that they would have a particular sex after consulting with an astrologer.

Boy babies were particularly valued as many poor families depended on them for future income, while girls would leave the family to marry. At the top end of the social scale the birth of a son was also seen as vital to provide an heir, particularly in respect of royalty. Henry VIII is the perfect example of a monarch desperate for a son. When his second wife, Anne Boleyn, entered her eighth month of pregnancy the King ordered that one of his treasures, a beautiful bed covered with a satin canopy and fringed with gold, 'one of the most magnificent and gorgeous beds that could be thought of', be moved into her apartments. He was confident that the unborn child was a boy and it seemed appropriate that such a bed be used. Two cradles were prepared for the future heir: one 'great cradle of estate' upholstered in crimson cloth of gold, and a carved wooden cradle painted gold.

During the Queen's labour courtiers assembled in the adjoining chamber discussing names, and they were pleased that the boy would be a Virgo, given to stern judgement. The anxiety Anne felt as she entered labour must have been compounded by the fear that she would produce a child of the wrong sex. Upon realisation that the baby was in fact a girl, later to become Queen Elizabeth I, horror and fear swept through the birth chamber in anticipation of the King's reaction.

Midwives

It was widely accepted for most of history that women knew instinctively what was best for women in labour. The success rate of midwives appears to have been high compared with that of doctors. Home deliveries were infinitely safer than those in hospital, as hygienic practices were not followed by doctors and nurses who had little knowledge of bacteria and cross-infection. The 'old wives' were much more patient and also less likely to interfere, they seldom used instruments, and rarely inserted their hand inside a labouring woman, unlike the male doctors. Their technique was natural, which in turn meant fewer complications, and the midwives' patients had great confidence in them.

Midwives were vital and generally well-respected members of the community. Despite the suspicion with which church leaders regarded midwives, particularly during the seventeenth and eighteenth centuries, most were respectable married women, almost all churchgoers, with years of practical experience. For most midwives, attending a woman during childbirth was a labour of love, and their payment would often be just a few pennies or sometimes payment in kind, such as a chicken or piglet. However, there is evidence that midwifery could be a lucrative business, particularly if called to care for those in noble families: the French midwife who attended Henrietta Maria, wife of Charles I, was paid £1,000. Godparents occasionally tipped the midwife too; the diarist Samuel Pepys paid the midwife who delivered his godchild ten shillings.

Although midwifery was free from domination by male doctors during this period, midwives were not free of interference from the religious authorities and were often scrutinised by clergy who were afraid that they may not have held genuine religious beliefs. In 1591 the midwife Agnes Simpson was burned at the stake for trying to relieve birth pains with opium: God was being deprived of the earnest cries from women who would beg for mercy in their agony.

Many midwives were suspected of using dubious methods to aid a woman in her travail, although much of the suspicion arose from men of the cloth rather than other members of society. Churchmen worried that midwives might use old practices associated with magic to relieve a woman's suffering during childbirth. Protestants were strongly opposed to the use of magic and charms and tried to prevent superstition ruling people's daily lives.

Apart from the controversy over pain relief, resentment continued from churchmen because, alone among women, midwives occasionally performed a priest-like function, administering the sacrament of baptism to a baby who seemed likely to die. The Synod of Triers, an ecclesiastical council held in 1277, ordered that midwives should be taught to perform baptism on any child who appeared too sickly to survive long enough to be baptised by a parish priest. Following the Reformation the Anglican Church continued to permit midwives to perform baptism. Some clergymen would have preferred to risk the souls of young infants rather than hand such responsibility over to a woman.

It was also felt that a woman in childbirth was vulnerable to supernatural forces, and many midwives were suspected of practising witchcraft. The caul (the membrane covering the newborn's head), placenta and umbilical cord were rumoured to be treasured ingredients for the cauldron, and a stillborn child was also important in the rites of witchcraft. Members of the clergy suspected that many midwives chose their profession in order to facilitate their double lives as witches, and there are records of midwives being executed for allegedly murdering newborn babies and dedicating their souls to the Devil.

The Church authorities tried to overcome the widespread use of traditional rituals during childbirth by replacing them with prayers and religious exercises to ensure that childbed attendants adhered to Christian practices and values. Midwives were encouraged to use prayers to sustain patients through their travails, and midwives would sometimes mark each corner of the house with a cross and recite the following prayer:

> There are four corners to her bed
> Four angels at her head:
> Matthew, Mark, Luke and John;
> God bless the bed that she lies on.
> New moon, new moon, God bless me.
> God bless this house and family.

In an effort to control their behaviour the religious authorities made midwives sign oaths, an idea that originated during the Middle Ages; the first known of which was in Regensburg, Germany, in 1452. Midwives were unable to obtain their license to practice if they refused to sign the oath.

Midwives were subordinated to the parish priest upon signing their license, in which they had to agree to various conditions such as those shown in this passage from *The Book of Oaths*, 1689:

You shall swear, first, that you shall be diligent and faithful, and ready to help every woman labouring of child, as well the poor as the rich; and that in time of necessity you shall not forsake or leave the poor woman to go to the rich [...] You shall not suffer any woman's child to be murdered, maimed or otherwise hurt [...] That you shall not in any wise use or exercise any manner of witchcraft, charm or sorcery.

Wealthy midwives were the exception rather than the rule, and unfortunately most practising midwives earned little income and could not afford to pay for the license offered by the Church. They continued to work despite the risk of being excommunicated if they were discovered. The main concern for the Church was the character of the midwives applying for licences; little attention was paid to their competence for the job.

Despite swearing their belief in Christian values, suspicion of midwives continued. Ignorance of the workings of the female body and the wonder of birth only added to the fear of the mysterious and secret world of midwifery. Throughout the centuries the skill of midwives was gained with experience and passed down the generations. Most midwives lacked formal training. With the development of printing a number of new books on the care of childbearing began to appear, most perpetuating ancient advice. The most popular was *A Rose Garden for Pregnant Women and Midwives*, published in Germany in 1513 by Eucharius Rösslin. The first English edition was dedicated to Catherine Howard, fifth wife of Henry VIII. Translated in 1545 by Thomas Raynalde and renamed *The Byrthe of Mankynde*, it was a mixture of half-truths and oddities, but was assumed at the time to be an authoritative guide. Although intended as a guide for midwives, it would have largely been useless as the majority of them were illiterate.

One of the first schools for midwives opened in Paris in the sixteenth century: the Hôtel Dieu, where hundreds of women delivered their babies, and by the mid-seventeenth century it was well known all over Europe. Despite the dirty conditions in the hospital, which was attached to the medical school, the experience gained by the staff and the focus on training resulted in midwives armed with far superior skills than their British counterparts.

A leading French midwife of the seventeenth century was Louise Bourgeois, who had studied at the Hôtel Dieu. She trained new midwives and wrote three obstetric textbooks. It is in one of these books that the first recorded description of cross-infection can be found. On account of her reputation she was appointed as royal midwife and attended the birth of Louis XIII, son of Queen Marie de Medici, in 1601. A total of two hundred people attended the birth, and when the baby was born Louise Bourgeois took wine into her own mouth then blew it into the baby's throat to soothe his distress.

Louise Bourgeois was one of the few women during this period who were either able or given the opportunity to publish authoritative guides on any subject, even obstetrics, despite women being the main caretakers and overseers of the birth process. Even those women who were privileged with an education lacked the social status necessary to be taken seriously, although there were exceptions. It was generally accepted, however, that labour was a woman's domain and midwives often cited the Bible to assert their rightful place in the birthing chamber; throughout the entire Bible there is not a single mention of a man attending childbirth.

In the mid-seventeenth century Percival Willughby began practising in England. He was one of the first male midwives, and, in *Observations in Midwifery*, wrote of his female counterparts:

> I have been with some that could not read, with several that could not write and with many that understood very little practice, and for such as these be, it would do no good to speak of them of anatomising the womb.

Although male midwives did not gain popularity immediately they were often considered by the middle-classes to be better attendants due to their superior education. The introduction of specialised obstetrical instruments posed a real threat to female midwives who usually lacked both knowledge of and access to these innovations, paving the way for male domination of the birthing process.

Until the seventeenth century men only became involved in childbirth if the need for surgery arose, however, the popularity of the Chamberlen brothers following their invention of the forceps in the early part of the century meant that male midwives became sought after by many women of standing. Word spread that the brothers were able to shorten labours and extract a baby live from a difficult birth, although they would not reveal their secret to the world. Due to their elaborate attempts to conceal the design of their instruments it was to be a further hundred years before their family invention was made public in 1733. In order to maintain mystery and guarantee their popularity among the rich, the brothers arrived at each confinement with a huge wooden box. They would force the midwife to leave, blindfold the labouring woman and then create great noise and commotion by ringing bells and slapping wooden sticks so that nobody would hear the sound of the metal forceps.

> Thou know'st, the first time that we smell the air,
> We wawl and cry [...] When we are born, we cry that we are come
> To this great stage of fools.
> – William Shakespeare, *King Lear*, 1606

Although guarding their secret proved a great disservice to the majority of women who were unable to afford their services, the brothers were committed to improving the standards of midwifery in Britain to match those on the Continent. They proposed a plan to train midwives, but it was rejected both by the midwives themselves and the College of Physicians, who felt that the brothers were only interested in making money. There were others who tried to initiate formal training for midwives during the seventeenth century, such as the Catholic midwife Elizabeth Cellier, but like earlier attempts hers too fell by the wayside.

Unfortunately, lack of formal training further undermined the position of women as midwives during the next one hundred years. Not only were midwives refused access to instruments such as forceps, but also their lack of formal training was blamed for the spread of puerperal fever. In fact, the disease was spread by doctors who would insert their hands into a labouring woman without washing them after conducting post-mortems. Constant rumours and speculation about the dubious activities of some midwives, such as performing abortions and running lying-in homes for prostitutes, meant women became increasingly likely to employ a male midwife. Women with an education were not attracted to midwifery because of the disreputable nature of the profession and lack of financial reward, perpetuating still further the 'old crone' image of midwives.

A Woman's Travail

As a woman approached the end of her pregnancy she would turn her attention to the setting in which she would give birth. With the help of her female friends and relatives she would prepare clean clothes, fresh bedding and any other equipment she might need during the trial ahead. Windows were covered as the birthroom was supposed to be kept warm, dark and snug for labour and the lying-in period following the birth. This atmosphere was believed to have the added benefit of restricting entry to evil spirits.

Women placed enormous trust and reliance in each other during this difficult time. After all, two lives were at stake during birth. One lady, Elizabeth Josceline, wrote down advice for her children in case she died in childbirth, to obviate the 'loss my little one should have, in wanting me'. Sadly she died nine days after the birth. Her writings were printed as *The Mother's Legacy to her Unborn Child* in 1625.

The influence of religion on the whole of society remained strong, and people relied heavily on their beliefs during times of trouble. Many prayers were recited in an effort to bring women safely through childbirth, and prayers were printed for the entire country to recite during royal pregnancies. When Queen Anne became pregnant in 1605, James I of England had prayers printed to preserve her from the dangerous journey ahead of her and appointed them to be used in church morning and evening by every minister until his wife's safe deliverance. Congregations prayed to God that 'through thy heavenly protection she may be safely delivered of the blessed fruit of her body, and become a joyful mother of a happy issue'.

Although women entered labour praying that they would survive the event, many of those who suffered complications hoped that they would die to avoid the prolonged agony of continuing in labour. Midwives were not inclined to intervene in the birth process and consequently some women entered their second, third or even fourth day of labour praying to be released from their misery, even if it meant death.

The Birth of Mankynde encouraged midwives to treat labouring women attentively and with gentle care. According to the text a midwife should:

sit before the labouring woman and shall diligently observe and wait, how much and after what means the child stireth itself. Also shall with hands anoynted with the oyle of those white lillies, rule and direct everything as shall seme best. Also the midwife must instruct and comfort the party not only refreshing her with good meat and drink, but also with sweet words giving her hope of a good speedie deliverance, encouraging and enstomacking her to patience and tolerance, bidding her to hold her breath as much as she may, also stroking gently with her hands her belly about the navel for that helps to depress the birth downward.

Percival Willughby advocated the gentle approach to childbirth:

> The midwife's duty in a natural birth is no more but to attend and wait on Nature, and to receive the child, and (if need require) to help to fetch the afterbirth, and her best care will be Nature's servant. Let them always remember that gentle proceedings (with moderate warm-keeping, and having their endeavours dulcified with sweet words) will best erase and relieve and soonest deliver their labouring women.

There were a number of tricks used by midwives in order to encourage a speedy delivery. They would often apply warm cloths to the stomach, partly to relieve pain but also to rub the baby downwards. Enemas were often given, which had the effect of widening the birth canal. Ergot, a plant fungus, was an effective drug that increased uterine contractions. Sneezing powder was occasionally used as it was thought that sneezing could help to push the baby out.

Take a loc of vergins haire on any part of ye head, of half the age of ye woman in travill, cut it very small to fine powder, then take 12 ants' eggs, dried in an oven after ye bread is drawne, or otherwise make them dry and make them to powder with the haire, give this a quarter of a pint of red cow's milk or for worst of it give it in strong ale wort.
– Zerobabel Endicott, *Remedy for Sharpe and Difficult Travel in Women With-child*, 1670

In the absence of pain relief, women took various measures to lessen the intensity of labour pain and childbirth's accompanying peril. Many people would use special sayings, applications of sympathetic magic and a variety of concoctions to bring a woman safely through her labour. Herbal medicines were also used that included lilies, roses, cyclamen, sowbread, columbine and aquilegia, all of which were thought to be helpful. If there were problems during the birth, the liver of an eel was sometimes given to the patient in powder form. While many of the remedies used by midwives would have had little if any medicinal benefits, their placebo value cannot be underestimated, particularly as so many people placed great faith in magic and superstitions despite the best efforts of the Church.

Magic girdles, which were manuscripts rolled and tied to pieces of cord or string, were popular as aids to women's ailments: they were used for relieving menstrual cramps, preventing miscarriage, overcoming infertility, and easing pain during childbirth. The string was tied around the waist or hips, and sometimes cowry shells, which resembled the vulva, were tied to girdles as these too were thought to be helpful in promoting an easy labour. Some families passed their magic girdle down the generations to be used by all the female members during labour. In 1536 a convent in Bruton was reported to keep 'our Lady's girdle of Bruton, red silk, which is a solemn relic, sent to women travailing which shall not miscarry in partu'.

As men entered the birthing arena women began to take a recumbent, rather than an upright position to give birth, possibly because it was more convenient for the men who attended them. Percival Willughby wrote of the care he believed women should receive:

> Let me persuade and entreat the midwife not to torment the poor
> woman, at the first coming of her pains, by putting her head to kneel,
> or to sit on a woman's lap, or on the midwife's stool, but to suffer her
> to walk gently or lie down on a truckle bed.

As women took to their beds for delivery the most favoured position was lying on the edge of the bed with thighs drawn up and the midwife behind. This position not only allowed a woman to maintain her dignity by revealing as little of herself as possible, but also kept out of her view any nasty-looking instruments that may have been used during the delivery. Although women were advised to lie down for delivery they were encouraged to remain mobile during the first stage of labour in order to maintain regular contractions.

Once a baby was born one of the first jobs for the midwife was to sever the umbilical cord. She would use her knife, one of her most important tools, and this became a standard emblem of her office. The physical separation of mother and child became a ritual surrounded by many beliefs and superstitions. Some people held that the future size of an adult's penis or the tightness of the vagina depended on the length of umbilical cord the midwife left. It was also believed that the navel held the key to future fertility. If the baby's navel was wrinkled then the mother would have many more children to come. Some people carried a piece of umbilical cord around in order to deter illness, witchcraft and devils.

Occasionally a baby was born with a piece of afterbirth membrane covering their face, which was known as a caul. It was removed following birth and laid on paper to dry. The caul was thought to bring great fortune and was highly prized. It was also thought that the health of the original owner could be determined by examination of the caul; if it was crisp and dry the baby was well, but being damp and flabby indicated poor health. Cauls were believed to protect against drowning, so they became sought after by sailors and were advertised for sale at very high prices.

Difficult Deliveries
There were many birth complications that struck fear into the heart of a labouring woman and the loved ones surrounding her. One of the most feared was malpresentation of the child. In the days before safe Caesarean sections the sight of a leg, arm, bottom or, worst of all, face first caused many birth attendants to panic. It was not unknown for a woman in this situation to be abandoned to her fate. Although most breech births were delivered naturally, a face presentation or transverse lie (where the baby is positioned crosswise in the womb) proved extremely difficult to deal with, and if the midwife was unable to correct the position both mother and baby usually died.

Rickets caused a large number of women to suffer prolonged labours. Many female children reached adulthood with a malformed pelvis that obstructed natural delivery. Percival Willughby noted that, 'The wild Irish do break the pubic bones of the female infant, so soon as it is born [...] and that they have ways of keeping these bones from uniting. It is for certain that they be easily and soon delivered. And I have observed that many wanderers of that nation have had a waddling and lamish gesture in their going'.

If delivery of an infant was obstructed in some way there was little that could be done to correct the situation safely. Often brute force was the only way of freeing a poor woman from her dilemma but it almost always ended in disaster. Birth attendants would grasp whatever part of the baby presented itself and simply pull. Percival Willughby visited three midwives who had cut off a baby's arm in order to deliver it, then strapped the arm at its side using a shirt:

'It was so well done and shrouded that to one who knew nothing and had only looked on the child's body, thus shrouded, this ill work at a distance could not have been perceived that the arm was cut off at the shoulder.'

Techniques differed around the world and though efforts to separate a mother and infant in England were unsophisticated to say the least, they were preferable to those employed in other parts of the Europe. In Hungary, for example, if a woman experienced difficulty during labour her husband would step over her three times, then fumigate her vagina by burning either his underpants or hair from his and her armpits. If this failed to shift the infant he would proceed to make love to her, contractions or no contractions!

It is not surprising that women in such situations preferred to die rather than endure the torture of well-meaning individuals' offers of help. Those who remained conscious as their labours continued in vain had to tolerate what was seen as a last ditch method of delivery: violent physical action. Some mothers were held upside down and shaken violently or wrapped in a blanket and tossed. If these actions were ever successful both mother and child would undoubtedly have suffered permanent problems both physical and emotional.

Alternatively, barber-surgeons would perform a craniotomy (piercing of the baby's skull in order to pull it out) or embryotomy (dismembering the baby to remove it) using sharp instruments. Obviously these methods were used as a last resort because they involved dismembering the baby piece by piece. The experience must have been harrowing for the birth attendants, not to mention the mother, and one which was avoided if at all possible.

In an attempt to avoid the death of an infant some barber-surgeons performed a pubiotomy to relieve constriction in the pelvis. This involved sawing through the pelvic bone followed by a symphisiotomy, which divided the junction of the two pelvic bones. The pubic bones then had to be separated by at least two inches to allow any chance of removing the fetus, and of course the mother would be left disabled for life, unable to walk and probably incontinent.

Thankfully the days of butchers' hooks and other terrifying methods to remove a wedged fetus came to an end once the design of forceps became widely known.

In experienced hands forceps were used with great success. For the first time midwives could assist mothers in delivering a baby who was malpresented or stuck in the pelvic cavity, and the baby would have had a good chance of survival. Unfortunately they were often used by the unskilled and terrible damage was sometimes inflicted, as the following report written by the midwife Lisbeth Burger demonstrates. She assisted the father of the child in restraining the mother while a doctor used forceps to aid delivery:

> The groaning and whimpering of the mother dominated everything in the room, the jerking and shaking of her tortured body [...] After all that pulling and levering, holding and bleeding, the child finally emerged from the mother's lap. Torn and haemorrhaging, exhausted to death, the poor mother lay back against the cushions.

If a child was safely delivered relatives began to celebrate and thank God that the mother had survived the birth, but sadly there were other complications that could occur after delivery. Haemorrhage presented grave danger for mothers and could be caused by prolonged labour or clumsy removal of the placenta. Cold compresses were sometimes used to try and stem the flow of blood. The most successful treatment was to administer ergot, which caused the uterus to contract. Midwives appreciated the benefit of ergot long before doctors.

One of the biggest killers of new mothers, however, was puerperal fever (systematic bacterial infection and septicaemia). Sometimes the fever gained control of the body so slowly that it remained unnoticed for up to a week after delivery. It was often thought that the mother and child had safely passed through childbirth after this length of time, then the mother would quietly slip away without a struggle. Fevers were also caused by mastitis, an inflammation of the breasts, also known as milk fever. Milk fever was popularly thought to be caused by milk leaving the breasts to enter the blood.

Another dangerous complication was infection of the uterus, which, if it spread to the blood and abdomen, threatened the mother's life. If this happened there was little that could be done to save her. Many women suffered horrendous pain if the bacteria reached the lining of the abdomen, causing peritonitis.

Lying-in hospitals were opened in the seventeenth century in an effort to help such women. Unfortunately the hospital wards were often so filthy that they were more dangerous than almost any other environment. Jacques Rene Tenon's description of the Hôtel Dieu from 1788 highlights the septic condition of hospitals during this period: 'little alleys and dim passageways among them, where the walls are covered with spittle, the floor covered by the filth that drains from the mattresses and from the commodes when they're emptied, as well as with the pus and blood that pour down from wounds or bloodlettings.'

The spread of infection was not understood, and consequently those mothers with fevers were not isolated from those without, sufferers of venereal disease often shared wards with new mothers, and even the morgue was not isolated from patients in some instances.

Family portrait from 1636 showing Sir Richard Saltonstall drawing back the curtains of the deathbed of his first wife. She gestures towards their two surviving children. His eyes, however, are on his second wife, who is holding her young baby

Medical Advances

Until the sixteenth century most of the medical knowledge possessed by doctors had been inherited from the Greeks and Romans, but, partly as a result of a terrible outbreak of syphilis, a new attitude to medicine began to emerge. Syphilis was thought to have been brought to Naples by Christopher Columbus's crew and was dubbed the 'Spanish', 'French' or the 'Neapolitan' disease.

It spread across Europe to England causing many deaths. Girolamo Fracastoro studied the devastating disease that caused skin eruptions and ulcerations and published his comprehensive study in *De Contagione* in 1546. This was the first-ever thorough observation of the spread of infections and marked a turning point in the field of medicine.

Many people began to realise that in order to gain any control over the diseases affecting the human body an accurate physiological knowledge was necessary. Emphasis was now placed on scientific detection rather than a reliance on the theories of ancient civilisations. In 1543 Andreas Vesalius published *The Fabric of the Human Body*. This text showed much of Galen's teaching to be erroneous and dissection of human bodies was seen as the way forward.

Medical progress inevitably followed. In 1628 the circulation of blood was documented by William Harvey. The Royal Society in London was excited by the findings of Harvey and extended their use of microscopes for further research. Three members of this society went on to achieve the first successful blood transfusion, although this was not perfected until blood groups were discovered, and consequently transfusions were abandoned until the nineteenth century. In 1683 Anton van Leeuwenhoek from Amsterdam spotted bacteria under a microscope, but it was generally thought to be a *result* of disease and not the *cause*; consequently diseases such as puerperal fever continued to take the lives of many new mothers. Gradually those in medical research paid greater attention to bacteria but it was not until the nineteenth century that a breakthrough was made in understanding infection.

Physiological knowledge of the human body steadily progressed as physicians freed themselves from the constraints of superstition and traditional schools of thought. The drive to study the precise workings of the human body continued and included efforts to understand the female body and the mechanics of labour. Old ideas regarding women were reconsidered and exact illustrations of the female anatomy were drawn, including one by Leonardo da Vinci.

A number of authoritative books emerged during the seventeenth century which brought the subject of obstetrics out of the realm of superstition and into the field of science. Englishman William Harvey's 1651 *De Generatione Animalium* contained first-hand accounts of real-life labours and practical advice that still stands today for those wanting labour to be less managed and more 'natural'; Harvey urged patience, gentleness, watchfulness and as little interference in the process of birth as possible. *De Generatione Animalium* was the first original book on midwifery in Britain and earned Harvey the title of the 'Father of British Midwifery'. Another rational and practical book was *Traite des maladies des femmes grosses et celles qui sont accouchees* by François Mauriceau, a former pupil of the Hôtel Dieu.

Increased urgency to discover new ways of treating disease arose in 1665 as a result of the plague. All attempts to find a cure had failed, with devastating consequences. The Great Fire of London in 1666 cleansed the city and burnt away all traces of the plague from the capital, but society at large remained in grave danger from numerous diseases and infections, mainly as a result of total ignorance of personal and public hygiene.

New Mothers

Following birth, mothers were expected to remain in bed for a minimum of nine days after delivery and were therefore unable to attend the baptism of their own child. In most cases their lying-in period was even longer than this. In the seventeenth century Margaret, Duchess of Wemyss, was advised of her daughter's intention to get out of bed fifteen days after the birth of her infant.

The Duchess was anxious and told her daughter, 'I pray God continue you in health, but it's not the way to be soon very well and strong, to try your strength too much. In this cold weather your bed had been better for you, I think.'

Midwives stressed the importance of the lying-in period for recovery and mothers were advised to lie flat in bed without moving. Such inactivity probably contributed to the high maternal mortality rates by allowing blood to coagulate and form fatal clots. Although the lying-in period was intended as a period of quiet rest, the mother was often surrounded by friends and family, all eager to celebrate not only the arrival of the new infant, but also the survival of the mother.

After a period of two or three weeks, if she was well enough, a new mother was bathed and changed and this marked the period of her 'upsitting' when neighbours arrived bearing gifts for yet more celebrations. A feast was often arranged by female friends.

Those mothers without outside help were of course unable to enjoy the luxury of such a long lying-in period and therefore resumed responsibility for the house and children after a couple of days. Religious sanctions ensured that new mothers were free from sexual advances from their husband, at least until they had been purified by churching. This short period at least allowed women the chance to physically recover from the birth.

Churching, the last ritual in the process of childbearing, marked a woman's return to everyday life. It was seen as a rite of reintegration after the ritual isolation of childbirth. It was a time for feasting and drinking, and most women looked forward to the occasion. They celebrated with the same women who had gathered around them for the birth and given thanks to God for their safe deliverance. After the Reformation, churching was seen as a way of thanking God for His blessing rather than for purification of the mother. The view from earlier centuries that churching was necessary to purify mothers following the loss of grace associated with childbearing was refuted by Puritan reformers who used the ceremony to welcome women back into the congregation. In an effort to rid the Anglican Church of Catholic beliefs and rituals, the traditional rite of churching was renamed 'The Thanksgiving of Women after Child-birth, commonly called the Churchynge of Women' in the 1552 *Book of Common Prayer*.

For those unfortunate mothers who were unmarried, churching could only take place once they had stood in front of the whole congregation on a Sunday and repented. As if the shame of carrying and delivering an illegitimate baby was not enough, they had to complete their humiliation in front of the entire village.

Once churched, a new mother's privileged month came to an end. She then had to cope with all the domestic duties, the young baby, and probably older children as well, although in many families female relatives would often help. It also brought an end to her right to celibacy; she would be expected to resume sexual relations with her husband. Without the benefit of birth control many women became pregnant very quickly after churching, and the dreaded cycle of pregnancy and birth continued.

Baptism

As soon as possible following birth, the baby would be taken by its father to church for baptism while the newly delivered mother remained at home. As principal governor of the household, the father of a newly born infant had chief responsibility for ensuring that a speedy baptism and accompanying feast was arranged. This was seen as part of his paternal duty, and if he delayed longer than eight days following birth he would face official charges. Fathers who refused to carry out this duty were prosecuted by an

Seventeenth-century portrait of 'Two Ladies of the Cholmondeley Family, Who were born the same day, Married the same day, And brought to Bed [gave birth] the same day'

ecclesiastical commission, and if they continued to neglect the infant's spiritual needs the child would be forcibly removed and taken to church for baptism in the father's absence. When Elizabeth and William Whiting of Cirencester, Gloucestershire, refused to baptise their baby in 1574 the minister and his churchwardens seized the child. Elizabeth and William were sent to prison in Gloucester, committed for their outright challenge to ecclesiastical authority, although Elizabeth was released after two weeks so that she could take care of her newly baptised child. Fathers were entitled to attend the baptism and often carried their infant into the church but were not permitted to speak during the service.

Almost everybody in Tudor and Stuart England was baptised in response to overwhelming cultural pressure. If any parent objected to baptism for their baby the priest would threaten to take the child by force to ensure that the gates of heaven would be open for them. There are a few recorded cases of parents who, being strongly opposed to the practice of christening, bravely took a stand against the authorities and refused to consent to baptism. In these few cases the fathers were jailed for a short period and their children forcibly baptised.

In view of the importance placed on baptism, early action was taken to ensure a speedy christening. The godparents, originally known as 'gossips' (derived from 'God sib', meaning relative of God), were summoned as soon as a woman went into labour. Custom called for two godfathers and a godmother for a boy, two godmothers and a godfather for a girl. During the baptism the godparents were expected to answer on behalf of the child when asked about forsaking the Devil and they were also to provide the child with a name when asked by the minister. They were then to ensure that their godchildren were brought up virtuously in Christian life.

Midwives continued to baptise babies when necessary, and the Bishop of London, Richard Bancroft, defended baptism by women when the Hampton Court Conference discussed this issue in 1604:

> the state of the infant, dying unbaptised, being uncertain, and to God only known; but if he die baptised, there is an evident assurance that it is saved; who is he that having any religion in him, would not speedily, by any means, procure his child to be baptised, and rather ground his action upon Christ's promise, than his omission thereof upon God's secret judgement?

If a child survived following baptism by a midwife it often caused problems for the clergy as, in the Bible, Paul tells the Ephesians, 'There is one body, and one spirit, even as ye are called in one hope of your calling; One Lord, one faith, one baptism.' Ministers were confused as to whether they should officially baptise the child in addition to the baptism performed by the midwife. Some

Protestant movements, known as Anabaptists, rejected infant baptism, insisting that adults be rebaptised. Those who disagreed with this belief felt that a further service risked collusion with the Anabaptists if the original baptism was valid, so a special service was devised by the Church authorities in which the priest would say, 'If thou be not baptised already, I baptise thee.'

This was not the only major dispute among Protestants regarding baptism. Many felt that the use of the cross during the service was scandalous as it was invented by man. The separatist John Canne was sickened by the use of the cross, blasting it as 'the mark of the beast, a juggler's gesture, a magical instrument, a rite and badge of the Devil, a harlot which stirreth up to popish lust'. Other disputes involved the use of water; whether the child should be totally immersed or how many times water should be sprinkled over the head. Some ministers would pour water over an infant's head three times, but others classed this as a distasteful ritual, not based in scriptural fact.

Fathers

For most parents, the birth of their baby is the most important event in their lives. Childbirth is a time of extreme physical challenge for the mother, but it is emotionally challenging for both parents. The image of fathers in days gone by tends to be of a distant figure who would pat their children on the head as they went up to bed and share an occasional chat during the evening meal.

Throughout the ages childbirth has been viewed as the domain of women in which men played very little part. Women relied on each other for support, sharing the pain and peril. Very few laymen ever entered the birthing chamber, and most had little idea of the process going on behind the scenes.

Hearing agonising screams during the birth, some men were astonished that their wives survived the event at all. They were ushered into the birthing chamber when it was all over and the midwife then presented them with the swaddled newborn. In accordance with tradition she often addressed the lucky man with the words, 'Father, see, there is your child, God give you much joy with it, or take it speedily to his bliss.'

> He must be swaddled to give his little body a straight figure, which is most decent and convenient for a man and to accustom him to keep upon his feet, for else he would go upon all fours as most other animals do.
> – François Mauriceau, *The Accomplish't Midwife*, 1673

Interestingly, most of the historical records relating to pregnancy and birth were written by wealthy or influential men in their role as either father, husband, doctor, or minister, as many ordinary men and women were illiterate and therefore unable to keep a written record of their own experiences. However, a few personal written records from fathers do survive, revealing the anxiety and fear that gripped the whole family when a woman entered labour. The diaries also demonstrate the affection between couples and the love they felt for their children.

> 'In going to my naked bed, as one that would have slept,
> I heard a wife sing to her child, that long before had wept.
> She sighed sore, and sang full sweet, to bring the babe to rest,
> That would not cease, but cried still in sucking at her breast.
> She was full weary of her watch and grieved with her child,
> She rocked it, and rated it, till that on her it smiled.
> Then did she say, 'Now have I found this proverb true to prove:
> The falling out of faithful friends, renewing is of love.'
> – Richard Edwardes, *Amantium Irae*, sixteenth century

Richard Rogers, a Puritan minister of Whethersfield, Essex, recorded his worst fears concerning his pregnant wife in his diary of 1588: 'I, seeing by much pain in wife and near childbirth many likelihoods of our separation, considered how many uncomfortablenesses the Lord had kept from me hitherto by those which I then saw must needs come if he should part us.' A later entry in his diary shows that his wife happily survived the birth.

Many men struggled to support their wives emotionally or contain their own fear of losing them during the birth. Ralph Josselin wrote of his wife's anxiety at the prospect of her labour in 1645. She 'was wonderfully afraid and amazed' and experienced 'great fears' during subsequent deliveries. During these deliveries Josselin placed his hope and trust in God to deliver his wife safely. 'My heart was sensible in some measure how great a loss it would be if God took her from me, and yet my spirit was borne up in expectation of the mercy.'

> The joys of parents are secret, and so are their griefs and fears.
> – Francis Bacon, sixteenth century

Isaac Archer, the vicar of Mildenhall in Suffolk, noted in his diary of 1670, 'my wife growing nearer her time was troubled with fears she should die, and I feared it too. She was much taken up. I saw, with such thoughts, and I was glad, because it was an occasion of seeking God.' A further entry in 1672 shows that Mrs Archer gave birth to another baby and experienced 'the very agonies of death, as she thought, and was seized all over with intolerable pain, and possessed with a persuasion she should die that night. Her father and mother were with her, and we all had grief enough'. Isaac Archer's diaries show that his wife survived nine births in all.

Frequent pregnancies obviously increased the risk of a man losing his partner, but as reliable contraception was unavailable the situation was difficult to avoid. Even uncomplicated births involved laborious travail, sharp pain and the prospect of lingering distress, and men realised that two lives were at stake: those of their wife and unborn child.

> Come little babe, come silly soul,
> Thy father's shame, thy mother's grief,
> Born as I doubt to all our dole,
> And to thy self unhappy chief:
> Sing lullaby and lap it warm
> Poor soul that thinks no creature harm.
> – Nicholas Breton, 'A Sweet Lullaby', sixteenth century

Following the birth, a husband would normally assume responsibility for the domestic duties during the lying-in period when the mother would withdraw from the outside world. As he went about organising household tasks he would have to tolerate almost constant visits from female neighbours and relations, who would provide round-the-clock companionship for his wife. It was the wife who specified which friends she wanted around her, and the husband who would set out to fetch them.

With many women around, the husband would lose the role of master in his own house. He would also have to find money to pay for the midwife to attend his wife during the birth. Men may not have understood the intimate mysteries of childbirth but they were in no doubt that their wives needed proper medical attention. Afterwards the husband would have to dig deeper into his pocket in order to pay for the festivities that accompanied the christening, upsitting and churching.

Although many fathers assumed a distant relationship with their children, fatherhood was seen as important and men were judged by their commitment to their family. Loyalty, above all else, was considered the mark of a true man and those who deserted their families were condemned. Just as modern fathers are pursued for maintenance, so men throughout the ages have been forced to provide financial assistance for their children. If an unmarried woman gave birth to a child, the secular and ecclesiastical authorities would investigate and if the father was identified he would have no choice but to assume financial responsibility for the child. If he was in a subordinate social position, such as a servant, he may have also been whipped. It was felt that every child should know its father, and paternity was the key to position and substance.

When we think of the families of previous centuries we often imagine a lack of feeling towards the young, with children being dragged rather than brought up. History books describe the harsh lives of people in previous centuries and the absence of a carefree childhood for most. Although this may have been the case, parents were merely victims of the circumstances in which they lived; young children were sent to work out of necessity rather than lack of sentiment. English parents gained a reputation for coldness towards their children that puzzled foreigners. In the Italian book *A Relation of the Island of England*, which described English customs in the reign of Henry VII, a diplomat wrote of how,

> the want of affection in the English is strongly manifested towards their children [...] having kept them at home until they arrive at the age of 7 or 9 years at the utmost, they put them out, both males and females, to hard service in the houses of other people, binding them generally for another 7 or 9 years.

However, some surviving poems and literature from this period reveal the strong feelings that existed between parents and their children, demonstrating that close bonds were formed between them from the moment they were born.

> I have given suck and know how tender 'tis to love the babe that milks me.
> – Lady Macbeth in William Shakespeare's *Macbeth*, 1606

Many of the manuscripts printed during the seventeenth century emphasised the importance of close contact between mother and child following the birth. According to *The Expert Midwife* of 1637 by Jacob Rueff, mother and child should be allowed a brief period together following birth in order to bond:

> Many say that the child being washed and wrapped in his swaddling clothes, before he suck the breasts or take any meat, must be laid by his mother, lying in her bed, on the left side near the heart first of all; for they think, as they are persuaded, that the mother doth attract and draw to her all the diseases from the child, and that she doth expel and void again by the flux and issue of her womb what evil soever she hath attracted, without any hurt to herself.

Once a baby had been safely delivered and laid beside its mother for a short while, both mother and child received an application of oils, powders, warm water and dressings. When both were comfortable, blessings and prayers were said for them.

> Sing lullaby, as women do,
> Wherewith they bring their babes to rest,
> And lullaby can I sing too
> As womanly as can the best.
> With lullaby they still the child,
> And if I be not much beguiled,
> Full many wanton babes have I
> Which must be stilled with lullaby.
> – George Gascoigne, 'Gascoigne's Lullaby', 1573

Suckling

Once born, babies were often comforted by a short period of closeness with their mother, and the lucky few were suckled at the breast soon after birth. Thomas Raynalde recommended that women 'abstain from venerie [sex] or man's company; for if she use that, it shall spend and consume the milk and make it unsavoury and unwholesome'. Many mothers though, particularly those from wealthy homes, were reluctant to nurse their own babies. Of the eighteen children Countess Elizabeth Clinton gave birth to, only one of her sons survived: the others were sent to unsuitable wet nurses. In 1662 the Countess wrote a pamphlet entitled 'The Countesse of Lincolnes Nurserie' in an effort to encourage other women to nurse their own children after realising the error of her ways. She recorded the various objections to breast-feeding given by women including, 'it spoilt the figure', was 'noisome to one's clothes' and 'interfered with gadding about'.

> Where yet was ever found a mother,
> Who'd give her booby for another?
> — John Gay, eighteenth century

When infants were sent away to nurse it was often a gamble as to what sort of home they would end up in. Wet nurses were judged on the size of their breasts and the colour of their cheeks rather than their suitability as temporary guardians of children.

> And I, for suckling, no fix'd hour prescribe;
> This Nature teaches best the nursing tribe:
> Let her our mistress be: and when, with cries
> The hungry child demands his due supplies,
> Forbear not you the wish'd relief to bring;
> Nor then be loath your snowy breast to bare,
> That he may suck, and streaming fragrance share.
> — Scevole de Sainte-Marthe, *Paedotrophia*, 1584

However, despite the popular belief that wet-nursing could change the natural disposition of the child and even alter its appearance to become more like the wet nurse, most wealthy women would simply not consider the possibility of feeding their own infants. Some believed it would be healthier for the infant to be fed by someone other than its mother. According to *The Byrthe of Mankynde*, 'it shall be best that the child suck not of the mother's breast by and by as soon as it is born, but rather of some other woman's for a day or two, for because that the cream, as they call it, straight after the birth, the first day in all women doth thicken and congeal'.

Wet nurses were highly sought after. It was mainly very poor women who offered themselves for this role, being entirely dependent on the income this would bring their family. It was believed that all sorts of moral qualities as well as physical nourishment passed from breast to lip. *The Byrthe of Mankynde* advised that a wet nurse should

> be of good colour and complexion, and that her bulk and breast be of good largeness [...] that it be not too long after her labour, so that it be two months after her labour at least, and that, if it may be, such one which hath a man child [...] that she be good and honest of conversation, neither over hasty or ireful, nor too sad and timorous: for these affections and qualities be pernicious and hurtful to the milk, corrupting it, and pass through the milk into the child, making the child of like condition.

Often infants from wealthy families would be sent away from home to live with their nurse, sometimes for a period of three years. The bewildered toddler would then have to cope with being sent back to his or her real parents, who must have wondered why the child then behaved in an unruly manner. The philosopher John Locke was also an influential writer on the welfare of children, and in *Some Thoughts Concerning Education*, published in 1693, he recorded the case of a mother who 'was forced to whip her little daughter on her first coming home from nurse, eight times successively the same morning, before she could master her stubbornness and obtain her compliance in a very easy and indifferent manner'. His sympathies were clearly with the mother.

In spite of the heartache such separation must have brought to many young children, wrenched from their adopted families by virtual strangers, by far the most distressing result of the hiring of wet nurses was the effect on the wet nurse's own baby. Parents preferred to send their infant to a nurse who had recently delivered her own child as her milk was considered to be fresher, and they often stipulated that she feed only their own baby as it was commonly thought that feeding two children would dilute the strength of the milk. The result of this lack of knowledge meant that the wet nurse's own baby would be subjected to the dangers of hand-feeding, and its own life would therefore be in jeopardy.

There were also many dangers associated with wet-nursing for the young charges. Some wet nurses would rub opium onto their nipples or mix opium in cordial drinks to keep the child quiet. Quite often too much was administered and the infant died as a result. Occasionally a wet nurse would then substitute her own child, who would be of a very similar age, to return to the wealthy household, concealing the fact that her nursling had died. Her own child would be given an opportunity of living a better life in a luxurious environment and she would escape accusations and blame from the family. These cases would account for the belief that babies bore a likeness to their wet nurse.

> If the child be strong and healthy, a year is enough in all conscience for it to suck [...] The fondness of mothers to children doth them more mischief than the devil [...] in letting them suck too long. Unnatural food in their infancy, and cockering in their youth, will (if it were possible) make a devil of a saint [...] When the teeth come forth, by degrees give it more solid food, and deny it not milk, such as are easily chewed [...] It is best to wean in the Spring and Fall in the increase of the moon, and give but very little wine.
> – Nicholas Culpeper, *A Directory for Midwives*, 1651

A number of books containing details of infant feeding were translated into English during the seventeenth century and all warned of the dangers of bending to the demands of the child. It was felt that if the baby was allowed to suck too often or for too long it would be vulnerable to a number of different diseases. In Michael Ettmuller's *Practice of Physic*, published in German, a common warning was reiterated: 'nothing is more apt to disorder the child than sucking it too often.'

This belief was directly contrary to the fact that children who were entirely breast-fed were the most likely to survive their infancy; records from foundling homes in England and France show an extremely high mortality rate for artificially fed infants. Sir Hans Sloan wrote of the horrendous mortality rates for dry nursed infants in 1660, which was 54 per cent compared to 19 per cent of breast-fed babies. Dry nursing involved feeding babies solid food such as gruel made from bread or flour mixed with water, in addition to cow's milk which was sometimes watered down. Difficulties with cow's milk also arose due to the lack of vitamin C and D it contained compared with breast milk, and so rickets was widespread. This was exacerbated by the fact that it was widely thought that fruit caused diarrhoea and was therefore never given to young children.

Childhood Ailments

Before the days of inoculations, antibiotics, analgesics and disinfectant, safely rearing a newborn into toddlerhood and beyond must have, at times, seemed an insurmountable task. Even ordinary childhood diseases and infections such as measles, scarlet fever or croup often proved fatal, but parents also had to deal with far more serious diseases such as smallpox, diphtheria and typhus. To make matters worse, when a child developed a fever all windows were sealed and a roaring fire lit. The feverish child would then be wrapped up and given hot drinks, often with disastrous consequences. High temperatures often lead to convulsions in young children and these seizures were a commonly recorded cause of death in infants during the sixteenth and seventeenth centuries.

Remedies were often ineffectual, disturbing, and sometimes even dangerous. A popular cure for thrush was to 'wrap a live frog in a cloth and place it under the child's mouth until it [the frog] is dead', advocated by John Aubrey's seventeenth-century *Cure for Thrush in Children*. The cloth was used to stop the child from swallowing the frog, although it was not always an effective prevention, hence the well-known expression 'a frog in the throat'.

Leeches were used right up until the nineteenth century for all manner of illnesses, placed strategically on various parts of the body depending on the patient's symptoms. If a child suffered from regular catarrh a leech was placed on the nose; croup required eight leeches on the windpipe; 'the watery gripes' called for leeches on the abdomen and, most unfortunately for little girls, urine infections required two leeches to be placed upon the vulva.

Old Wives' Tales
Never cut a baby's nails.
Always put a newborn baby in a drawer otherwise it is unlucky.
Good nut year, good baby year.
Squeezing milk into a baby's eyes prevents them from becoming sticky.
A donkey's hair worn round the baby's neck makes teething easier.
A baby weaned when the birds are migrating will have a restless temperament.
Never show a child under one its reflection in a mirror.
Children are blind until three months old.
It is unlucky for a baby to cut the upper teeth before the lower.
It is unlucky to name the child before its baptism.
Bathe the newborn baby in saltwater, and make it taste the water three times.

The sixteenth and seventeenth centuries saw the first break from medieval thought and practice concerning child-rearing. Fathers started to play a more important role in the upbringing of their children, and early education began to be seen as the cornerstone of a successful society. The Anglican Church encouraged parents to be diligent regarding their children's upbringing since the good order of the Church would be at stake when the children were grown. The condition of the child's soul was dependent on the efforts made by the parents to discipline and educate them. Catholic parents could rest at ease in the knowledge that their children's route to salvation was secured by baptism, but Protestant teaching that faith alone could save left parents feeling anxious.

These changes from medieval child-rearing practices paved the way for the emergence of a further degree of sensitivity towards children in the eighteenth century, though progress was to be slow.

4

TABOO, TORMENT AND TRAGEDY:

– THE EIGHTEENTH CENTURY –

THE EIGHTEENTH CENTURY marked the turning point in the health and welfare of the British public. Scientists began to unravel the mysteries of the human body, and as knowledge increased, the taboos that had been associated for many centuries with such intimate processes as pregnancy and childbirth gradually lost their importance.

Mystery still pervaded childbirth, however. In 1726 a woman named Maria Tofts claimed that she had been sitting in a field when she was frightened by a rabbit. She then proceeded to give birth to lots of rabbits that ran off into the field. The public heard news of this and flocked to witness the unusual event. Despite the scientific advances in some areas, people still thought it was possible for a woman to give birth to rabbits.

Old Wives' Tales

Horseradish applied to the breast prevents excessive lactation.

Lactating mothers should not put their hands in cold water, otherwise they will lose their milk.

Bathe breasts alternately with hot and cold water.

Steep mint in wine and oil and lay upon the nipples in a plaster to soothe sore breasts.

To prevent ephemeral fevers while lactating, wear blue woollen threads or cords around the neck. The cords are better if they are inherited from your mother – the older they are, the greater their powers.

Eighteenth-century Dutch lying-in room

Fertility and Pregnancy

Efforts to control fertility continued throughout the eighteenth century. The condom had been regularly used during lovemaking from the mid-sixteenth century and probably even earlier, although mainly to avoid contracting syphilis rather than as protection against pregnancy; however, it was only in the eighteenth century that their usefulness as a contraceptive became widely appreciated.

Condoms were usually made from linen, or the dried bladder or intestine of an animal. Where the condom got its name from is a mystery, although it may derive from the Latin *condere* meaning 'to protect'. A copy of *Tatler* from 1709 claimed that the sheath was given its name by 'A Gentleman of this House [Wills Coffee House] observ'd by the Surgeons with much envy; for he has invented an Engine for the Prevention of Harms by Love Adventures, and had, by great Care and Application, made it an immodesty to name his name.'

As using condoms for contraceptive purposes became more popular, manufacturers increased production and gradually improved the design. Linen condoms were generally regarded as awkward, and animal membrane tied with ribbon was often preferred. Ribbons of various colours were available to tie the condom at the bottom as it was seen as an attractive feature to decorate the penis with. Making the condoms involved an intricate and time-consuming process of soaking the animal membrane in alkaline solutions, then washing, scenting and polishing, and finally decorating with ornate ribbons. During the eighteenth century Britain became the largest manufacturer of condoms, exporting them all over the world.

In Scotland at the time a bride and groom would have their fastenings loosened in order to free any block to procreation, and this belief was also used in reverse as a contraceptive. The groom would tie knots in his handkerchief in order to avoid pregnancy. If only things were that simple.

Despite the growing popularity of contraceptives, there were still many couples who were either unaware of their availability or frightened of the spiritual consequences of limiting family size. Continuous, debilitating pregnancies remained a problem for many women. Fortunately as the years progressed greater attention was paid to health issues, and the welfare of childbearing women began to be considered a priority for the first time in history. Before the eighteenth century pregnant women were given very little advice on how to look after themselves and prepare for birth, except for an endless supply of old wives' tales that did little to allay a woman's fears. Alexander Hamilton, a Professor of Midwifery at Edinburgh, published his *Treatise of Midwifery* in 1781. The advice he gave differs little from recommendations made today to pregnant women. He believed that women should

> lead a regular and temperate life carefully avoiding whatever is to disagree with the stomach; they should breathe a free open air; their company should be agreeable and cheerful; their exercise should be moderate, and adapted to their particular situation; they should, especially in the early months when the connection between ovum and womb is feeble, avoid crowds, confinement, every situation which renders them under any disagreeable restriction.

Although most women, except those from middle- and upper-class families, were unable to rest during pregnancy due to economic constraints, they were nutritionally better off than previous generations. In the past both men and women had struggled to provide enough food for their families. Food production gradually improved during the eighteenth century, the country became better cultivated and drained, and agricultural techniques were refined. Increased potato and rye yields saw public health begin to improve significantly for the first time. Rye originated as a grain-field weed but became the most productive crop because it grows prolifically in any climate. Known as peasants' 'black wheat', it is an excellent source of iron, magnesium, selenium and riboflavin. Industrialisation hindered these gains in public health in the inner cities, however, due to overcrowding, squalor and poverty. People were often crammed into accommodation near factories in the centre of towns with no water or sanitation.

In spiritual matters, there had been improvements for childbearing women following the Reformation. The Protestant belief that pregnant women were not unclean in the eyes of God may have lessened their fears slightly, but women were still taught that they should repent of their sins following the first quickening, the moment when a mother can feel her baby stirring in the womb for the very first time. Moralists argued that it was this moment that should quicken a woman to repentance, believing that in that instant the baby inherits the guilt of Adam's sin. Some people believed that the forty-fifth day of pregnancy saw the birth of the soul, though others felt that body and soul become fused at conception.

As the Enlightenment dawned, science gradually replaced superstition. The race to improve medical care began and bit by bit the doors to a safer childbirth experience were opened.

Midwives
There existed a two-tier system of midwifery in the form of experienced urban midwives and their usually untrained and often totally illiterate rural counterparts. Regular midwives often had a trainee who served an apprenticeship before becoming a midwife herself. Experienced midwives were more knowledgeable about the birth process and female anatomy than doctors and were happy to hand their knowledge onto other midwives.

Most traditional 'granny' midwives were old women who had no other means of support and who turned to midwifery out of sheer necessity, providing a cheap alternative to doctors and experienced midwives. Rural midwives did not regard their work as a profession and had no knowledge of anatomy. Most practised part-time and muddled through by trial and error.

A step in the right direction came when young midwives in Britain, Germany and France began attending established schools in order to learn their trade and gain much needed experience before practising in the community. Unfortunately many granny midwives were reluctant to change their ways. They refused to attend school, but nevertheless remained a popular choice for poor families because they charged very low fees. Many mothers were only too pleased to employ old wives because although they lacked formal training they proved to be very helpful following birth, staying in the house to help care for the newborn and doing the household chores.

As the medical profession became more established, greater attention was paid to the care given by granny midwives, and criticism of their actions became more prominent. It was known that some old wives were often too eager to speed up delivery and would constantly stick their hands into the vagina, giving it a stretch and a pull in order to hurry along proceedings. Some old wives kept one fingernail very long in order to rupture the waters. Others would pull so hard on the umbilical cord once the baby was born that haemorrhage or inversion of the uterus resulted.

As the use of instruments during labour became more widespread, male midwives gained popularity, and their criticism of granny midwives further undermined the role of women as birth attendants. In 1742 Sir Fielding Ould, one of the first important teachers in the field of obstetrics in Ireland, published his *Treatise on Midwifery*, which contained a detailed and accurate study of labour. He was the first to advocate the use of episiotomy (cutting the perineum) to facilitate delivery and was also one of the first to prescribe pain relief during difficult labours.

One of the most notable male attendants during the eighteenth century was William Smellie, a Scot who had trained in Glasgow and Paris. Following training, he settled in London where he set up a shop near Pall Mall, advertising midwifery lessons for five shillings. He was eventually widely acknowledged as the master of British midwifery. He taught many hundreds of pupils in his London classes and attended over 1,000 labours. Although he advocated the use of forceps when necessary he claimed that out of 1,000 births he had only needed to use forceps ten times. Besides his obvious obstetrical skills, Smellie was a compassionate man with a social conscience and offered free care to impoverished women. It was his opinion that the greatest obstetric skills came from learning not to interfere with a labouring woman. During the time that William Smellie practised, taboos surrounding childbirth were still deep rooted in society, and if a man attended a birth he had to deliver the baby under a sheet to maintain the modesty of the mother.

Smellie's sensible rules were laid down and recorded in his *A Treatise on the Theory and Practice of Midwifery*, which was published in 1752. It also contained the first illustration of a pelvis deformed by rickets and a simple technique for measuring pelvic size. Smellie believed that the size of the baby in relation to the mother's pelvis was an important consideration in obstetrics; if the pelvis was badly contracted it was difficult for the mother to give birth naturally. In such cases, it was safer to deliver the baby by Caesarean section, avoiding the danger of the baby getting stuck in the birth canal.

Pelvic size was also considered important by Professor Jean-Louis Baudelocque of the Paris Maternité hospital. He brought great relief to many women by developing a way of measuring pelvic size externally. The usual form of measurement until this discovery was the insertion of a compass into the vagina, which often caused severe discomfort. The new technique was not only painless, but also allowed a woman to maintain her modesty.

Towards the mid-eighteenth century it was realised that improvements could be made to the instruments used during birth, particularly the forceps. William Smellie had always been distressed and saddened by the consequences of the incorrect use of forceps. One of his greatest achievements was to perfect the use of obstetrical instruments. His forceps were made of either wood or steel, and were padded with leather. He always insisted that they should only be used once the baby's head had entered the pelvis.

By combining their use with carefully calculated pelvic measurements he was able to reduce injury to both the mother and baby. Smellie was the first to realise that the fetal head rotated during labour, the first to apply the forceps to the aftercoming head in a breech delivery, and the first to revive an asphyxiated infant, which he did by inflating the lungs with a silver catheter.

Smellie's French counterpart André Levret was also keen to implement further improvements in obstetrical instruments, especially forceps, and took note of the advances made in this area by the doctors Edmund Chapman, William Giffard and Benjamin Pugh, who had all worked to modify the original design. Benjamin Pugh went on to publish his own *Treatise on Midwifery* in 1754 in which he asserted his belief that women should not assume a recumbent position during delivery. He felt strongly that gravity should be used to assist delivery and advocated a standing, kneeling or sitting position for the second stage of labour. He claimed that in his fourteen years of attending births he had never had to open a child's head (craniotomy) and all his patients had been delivered successfully.

Other male attendants such as Charles White, a prominent eighteenth-century midwife, worried about the effect of delivering in an upright position. He felt that it could be the cause of lacerations to the perineum and a number of other complications that could result in the death of the mother.

The Opening of Hospitals and Training of Doctors

Until the eighteenth century care of childbearing women took place mainly in the home. The realisation that medical care was wholly inadequate led to the opening of hospital schools. France continued to lead the rest of Europe during the eighteenth century, with the Hôtel Dieu being one of the largest training centres. The schools provided doctors with clinical training and gave medicine a scientific basis, moving it away from the realm of superstition. Women were still barred from medical training; doctors enjoyed exclusive status (despite offering largely inadequate treatments) and were not about to open their doors to the inferior sex. Such male dominance was reinforced by the patriarchal Christian religion, and widespread illiteracy in the general population meant there were few challenges to the status quo.

Following the popularity of formalised medical treatment, more lying-in hospitals were opened as the years progressed in an attempt to improve the care of childbearing women. Unfortunately they remained probably the most septic environments anywhere. Infections were rife, and the pain and misery suffered by women in labour was horrendous. Doctors in the Hôtel Dieu in Paris attended many hundreds of women in labour and quickly learned to identify cases of peritonitis, where bacteria had reached the lining of the abdomen. The

Eighteenth-century anatomical drawing of pregnant women

pain was often so severe that the patients could not even bear the pressure of a sheet on their abdomen. Those women who did recover from such an infection were often left with permanent damage, such as heart or kidney disease.

Towards the end of the eighteenth century doctors began to understand the causes of post-delivery sepsis or puerperal fever, but it was to be many years before preventative measures were implemented and longer still before any form of treatment became available.

In 1772 one of the worst epidemics of puerperal fever broke out in hospitals all over Europe, taking the lives of many thousands of women. It was estimated that at least 20 per cent of all newly delivered mothers lost their lives in this way. During the same year the midwife Charles White published a book concerning the treatment of women following childbirth. He noted the connection between lack of hygiene and fever and described the stagnant atmosphere surrounding many new mothers:

> As soon as she is delivered, if she be a person in affluent circumstances, she is covered up close in bed with additional clothes, the curtains are drawn round the bed and pinned together, every crevice in the windows and doors is stuffed closed, not excepting even the keyhole [...] and the good woman is not suffered to put her arm or even her nose out of bed for fear of catching cold. She is constantly supplied out of the spout of a teapot with large quantities of warm liquors to keep up perspiration and sweat, and her whole diet consists of them. She is confined to the horizontal position for many days together, whereby both the stools and the lochia [a discharge from the uterus] are prevented from having a free exit [...] The lochia, stagnating in the womb and the folds of the vagina, soon grow putrid.

White also noted that there appeared to be a widespread aversion to fresh air in the delivery room. 'When the woman is in labour, she is often attended by a number of her friends in a small room, with a large fire which, together with her own pains, throw her into profuse sweats; by the heat of the chamber, and the breath of so many people, the whole air is rendered foul and unfit for respiration.'

White felt that the best way to avoid problems following birth was scrupulous cleanliness, both of the birth attendants and any instruments used. He thought that mothers should be allowed to bathe following the birth and he was opposed to long lying-in periods, advocating that a woman should assume an upright position as soon as possible after delivery to allow the uterus to drain. One of his most revolutionary recommendations was that mothers should get up and move around on the second day after birth. Unfortunately, he was ahead of his time and many of his contemporaries disagreed with his suggestions.

The Spread of Infection

In Scotland the pioneering doctor and birth attendant Alexander Gordon realised that puerperal fever was spread from woman to woman by the attendants caring for her. He recommended that wards, clothing and bed linen be fumigated in order to prevent cross infection. Gordon wrote:

> I will not venture positively to assert that the Puerperal Fever and Erysipelas [a skin infection] are precisely of the same specific nature [but] that they are concomitant epidemics I have unquestionable proofs. For these two epidemics began in Aberdeen at the same time, and afterwards kept pace together; they arrived at the acme together, and they both ceased at the same time. After delivery the infectious matter is readily and copiously admitted by the numerous patulous orifices, which are open to imbibe it, by the separation of the placenta from the uterus.

Gordon sectioned three cases and found pelvic peritonitis. 'The disease seized such women only as were visited, or delivered by a practitioner [...] or nurse who had previously attended patients afflicted with the disease. It is a disagreeable declaration for me to mention that I was myself the means of carrying the infection to a great number of women.' Once again the suggestions were not taken seriously by the medical profession as a whole and the fever continued to break out in hospitals throughout the eighteenth century.

Despite the studies by a few doctors around Britain, hygiene and sanitation were, if anything, worse during the eighteenth century than in the previous one. Population growth meant that towns became overcrowded and little effort was made to prevent disease. When animals died their carcasses were often discarded in the streets and left to rot. Water supplies were often contaminated, causing dysentery and worms. Even dead human bodies were not always buried properly and the stench of decaying flesh permeated the air. There were many dreadful diseases to cope with, the most feared being smallpox. No treatment was available and survivors of the disease were left either blind or disfigured in some way.

Fortunately the knowledge of an inoculation against the pox, known in the Middle East for hundreds of years, spread to Britain via Lady Mary Wortley Montagu during the eighteenth century. Although a medical breakthrough, it was not understood why the procedure of injecting a small amount of the disease into a vein ensured protection against the disease.

Gradually the public became aware of the connection between lack of hygiene and disease, aided by men like Sir John Pringle, an army doctor who noted that fevers rarely broke out amongst troops in well-spaced and open camps. Following reports from the navy of improved health in sailors who enjoyed a better quality diet it was realised that poor nutrition could be responsible for a weakened constitution. Although there were no great improvements in medical treatment during the eighteenth century, as the next century approached it was at least appreciated that many diseases could be avoided by improving sanitation.

Dealing with Complications during Labour
Besides the dangers associated with infection, many mothers still

faced the possibility of haemorrhaging after the birth or permanent damage from the clumsy use of forceps. Although the use of forceps gradually became more widespread during the eighteenth century, there remained many occasions when birth attendants simply pulled on whatever part of the baby presented itself first. Occasionally attempts were made to enlarge the birth canal, such as by making deep cuts inside the suffering woman, but these usually ended in disaster.

William Smellie recorded a case of obstructed labour and was only too aware of the agony borne by the terrified woman involved:

> The arm had been pulled down by the midwife till the shoulder was at the vulva. Twenty-four hours later I was sent for, cut off the swollen arm, performed internal version and brought down one leg. This came off on pulling, so the other leg was brought down and the same thing happened again. Ultimately delivery was accomplished with the crochet. The woman behaved with great courage.

Caesarean sections were attempted as a last resort, and, although it is incredible that any woman could have survived the shock of such an operation before the invention of anaesthetic, there are several recorded cases where both mother and child lived to tell the tale.

One such occasion was a Caesarean operation performed in 1738 by an illiterate Irish midwife. She used a sharp razor to make a deep incision in the abdomen then 'held the lips of the wound together with her hand, till one went a mile and returned with silk and cotton needles which tailors used. With these she joined the lips in the manner of the stitch employed ordinarily for the harelip, and dressed the wound with whites of eggs'.

One of the next recorded cases appears to be in 1793, when Jane Foster from Manchester survived a Caesarean by Dr James Barlow but unfortunately the baby died. There followed a period during which several mothers and babies lost their lives, and opponents of the operation offered women symphysiotomy (dividing the junction of the two pubic bones) and the use of the hook to destroy the fetus. The Caesarean emerged as the lesser of two evils.

At this time the famous French obstetrician Jean-Louis Baudelocque published a book reviewing the thirty-one successful Caesarean sections that had been performed in the previous fifty years. A copy of the English translation of this book passed to Jesse Bennett, a doctor in Virginia, USA, who recorded that he had carried out a Caesarean section on his own wife in 1794. His wife survived and lived another twenty-five years and the child reached old age. The operation was done using laudanum, on two planks set across two barrels. Dr Bennett also removed both of his wife's ovaries so that they would not be subjected to such an ordeal again.

My God, prepare me for that hour
When most thy aid I want;
Uphold me by thy mighty power,
Nor let my spirits faint.

I ask not life, I ask not ease,
But patience thy submit
To what shall best thy goodness please,
Then come what thou seest fit.

Come pain, or agony, or death,
If such the will divine;
With joy shall I give up my breath,
If resignation's mine.

One wish to name I'd humbly dare,
If death thy pleasure be;
O may the harmless babe I bear
Haply expire with me.
     – Jane Cave, 'Written a Few Hours before the Birth of a Child',
                     eighteenth century

Despite the occasional successes, Caesarean operations only became safer once infections could be efficiently recognised and treated. The recommendations made by surgeon Charles White in 1772 and Doctor Alexander Gordon in 1775 in order to reduce the occurrence of puerperal fever were not generally adopted until the 1890s, and the use of antibiotics was not widespread until the twentieth century.

Newborns

> My mother groaned, my father wept.
> Into the dangerous world I leapt;
> Helpless, naked, piping loud;
> Like a fiend hid in a cloud.
> Struggling in my father's hands,
> Striving against my swaddling bands,
> Bound and weary I thought best
> To sulk upon my mother's breast.
> — William Blake, 'Infant Sorrow', 1789

With the pain and anguish of birth behind them, those women who had survived labour were able to breathe a sigh of relief and turn their attention to the newborn baby. Some mothers would feed their baby soon after birth, but this would be done with caution as there were still many who doubted the safety of too much breast milk.

Aversion to breast-feeding continued throughout the eighteenth century, although some mothers were swayed by those experts who were vociferous in their claims that mothers should feed their own infants. Novels such as *Emile* by the philosopher Jean-Jacques Rousseau also persuaded some mothers to breast-feed. In his book Rousseau described how he would raise a child and clearly disapproved of those mothers who refused to provide the most ideal food for their infants. His compassion did not extend to his own children, however, all of whom were consigned to a foundling hospital.

Many babies were subjected to the dangers of hand-feeding, which often proved fatal because of the dangers of unsterilised equipment and unpasteurised milk. Choosing to hand-feed a baby meant the child's chances of survival were negligible, yet many women, even those who were able to, were still not prepared to breast-feed. Astonishingly, records show that out of 10,000 infants hand-fed in the Dublin Foundling Hospital between 1775 and 1796, only 45 babies survived infancy, a mortality rate of 99.6 per cent. According to the London Bills of Mortality, 526,973 deaths out of a total of 1,178,346 deaths between 1730 and 1779 were children under the age of five.

> Bye O my baby,
> When I was a lady,
> O then my baby didn't cry;
> But my baby is weeping
> For want of good keeping
> O I fear my poor baby will die.
> – From *Gammer Gurton's Garland, or The Nursery Parnassus*, 1794

Babies who were brought up in the country had a better chance of survival than those in towns, simply because the milk was likely to be fresher, although mothers still had the problem of finding a suitable container from which the baby could suck. This was often overcome by holding the baby under an animal, usually a goat or donkey, to feed directly. In 1775, Dr Alphonse Leroy, a medical reformer, described how infants in the Foundling Institution in Aix were fed:

Nineteenth-century sketch by John Scarlett Davis entitled Death of an Infant
after an earlier seventeenth-century work

Each goat which comes to feed, enters bleating into the ward, and goes to hunt the infant which has been given to it, pushes back the covering with its horns and straddles the crib to give suck to the infant.

The use of containers greatly increased the danger of hand-feeding infants, since it was extremely difficult to keep them clean. A hollow cow's horn was often used, with a hole in the tip covered with parchment or leather. As the baby sucked, milk would seep through the tiny holes made by the stitching. If the baby wanted more milk the nurse could easily refill the horn through the open end. Infants fed through a horn were at an advantage, as any left over milk could not be stored and was therefore poured away. When bottles were used, milk was often kept for hours between feeds and would then be teeming with bacteria.

> The invention of horns, sucking bottles, and many other contrivances for artificial nipples, are too lame and imperfect imitations of nature to be useful [...] as these machines cannot be kept perfectly clean.
> – Thomas Mantell, *Short Directions for The Management of Infants*, 1787

In an effort to curb the shocking infant mortality rates, authorities in some countries attempted to encourage mothers into nursing their own children. In the Vasa district of Sweden in 1753, for example, the governor received permission from the king to fine mothers who refused to breast-feed. Concern for the wet nurse's own children led to a law in France in 1762 stating that a woman could not take on a nursling until her own infant was nine months old. It was estimated in 1780 that out of 21,000 babies born each year in Paris, only 1,000 were actually nursed by their own mothers. Over 17,000 infants were sent to the countryside to be nursed, which led to regulations being passed to protect the babies en route: a nurse must always travel with them, and there must be a reasonable depth of fresh straw on the floor of each cart.

Let the twin hills be white as mountain snow,
Their swelling veins with circling juices flow;
Each in a well-projecting nipple end,
And milk in copious streams from these descend.
— Scevole de Sainte-Marthe, *Paedotrophia*, 1584

A fashionable eighteenth-century mother wearing a dress with slits across the breasts in order to feed her baby

The frequency of feeds was often debated. In his 1749 *Essay upon Nursing and the Management of Children*, William Cadogan advised that infants should only be fed four times every twenty-four hours, but by 1792, when *Mothercraft Manual* was published by H. Smith, four-hourly feeds were being recommended. Sticking to such a strict regime must have proved difficult, since generally breast-fed babies demand more frequent feeds. Many babies would be desperate for milk after such a long interval and would consequently suck fiercely on the nipple. This would cause nipple soreness and a vicious circle would result. Perhaps this is one of the reasons why breast-feeding was so unpopular.

Weaning was another aspect of infant feeding that caused extreme disagreement and contention. Some experts believed that weaning should begin as soon as possible, as concurred by Dr William Buchan's *Domestic Medicine* of 1776: 'After the third or fourth month it will be proper to give the child once or thrice a day, a little of some food that is easy of digestion; as water pap, milk pottage, weak broth with bread in it and such like'.

Pap was made using a mixture of flour or bread, cooked in water. Sometimes beer or wine would be added. If the consistency was too thick it was often diluted with saliva and placed directly from the nurse into the infant's mouth. Alternatively pap was fed to the baby using a spoon or 'pap-boat'. The oval-shaped pap-boat appeared during the eighteenth century and its contents was often poured down an infant's throat rather than spooned into their mouth.

Dr Hugh Smith launched his own design in 1777 in protest at the forced feeding which often accompanied the use of pap-boats. His 'Bubby Pot' was specially designed so that the baby had to suck its own food and he claimed that even 'nurses confess [it] is more convenient than a boat'. He proudly describes the pot in the

1792 edition of his *Letters to Married Women on the Nursing and Management of Children*:

> In short, it is upon the same principle as those gravy pots which separate the gravy from the oily fat. The end of the spout is a little raised, and forms a roundish knob […] this is perforated by 3 or 4 small holes, a piece of fine rag is tied loosely over it, which serves the child to play with instead of the nipple, and through which, by the infant's sucking, every drop he receives.

The use of pap was condemned by some experts; in 1783 Dr De Claubry, a French paediatrician, advised nurses that 'pap is the most dangerous of all the foods for infants, that it has caused to perish a great number or has rendered them infirm and diseased their whole lives'.

Eighteenth-century print of a child in a high chair

Growing Up in Eighteenth-Century Britain

Mothers usually assumed total responsibility for childcare during earlier centuries, with some assistance from female relatives and friends, and perhaps older children. Wealthy parents did not concern themselves with the messy business of caring for their own children, however, preferring to use their servants as childminders.

Various contraptions were used by harassed mothers and childminders in order to keep their charges quiet while they got on with other household duties. The standing stool, made from a hollowed-out tree trunk, proved to be a popular piece of furniture in the nursery. A young baby, from the age of about six months, would be propped up inside the cylinder, unable to move and therefore safely out of harm's way. As a temporary measure it may have amused a young baby, but many were restrained in the stool for hours on end by careless minders.

Very poor mothers who could not enjoy the luxury of staying at home to care for their own baby had to find a cheap solution to the problem of childcare. Local dame schools charged modest fees, and although they were intended to provide lessons for those old enough to learn, the teachers were often willing to mind younger children and babies. To overcome the problem of toddler escapees, the old dame would sometimes tie the young charges to her chair or to her skirt, hence the old saying 'tied to a mother's apron strings'.

As the eighteenth century progressed, bringing increased industrialisation, mothers were often forced through poverty to work long hours in the new manufacturing towns, and affordable childcare became even harder to find. Desperate mothers would leave their young infants in the care of old women who would take in as many children as possible for a very small fee. Caring for so many babies at a time was physically impossible for an elderly woman, and laudanum was often used to sedate her charges, which inevitably claimed the lives of thousands of children each year.

Babies and children who were not lucky enough to be part of a family fared even worse than those from poverty-stricken homes. These children depended on charity for their care and became the responsibility of the parish overseer. Parishes, keen to keep their expenses to a minimum, often employed the services of a nurse, paying her one year's board in advance to care for the baby. This became one less problem for the parish to worry about, and the fact that these babies seldom survived for long once payment had been received was largely ignored.

> I have been assured by a very knowing American of my acquaintance in London, that a young healthy child well nursed is at a year old a most delicious, nourishing, and wholesome food, whether stewed, roasted, baked, or boiled, and I make no doubt that it will equally serve in a fricassee, or a ragout.
> – Jonathan Swift, *A Modest Proposal*, 1729

Parishes also employed foster parents, many of whom were happy to offer their homes to as many orphans as possible so that as the infants grew older they could be used as a means of generating income. In 1761 Anne Martin was sentenced to two years' imprisonment for deliberately blinding children in order to use them for begging. The leniency of the sentence demonstrates the lack of regard for children in eighteenth-century society, including in law. When prosecuting children, however, it was deemed fair to treat them as adults from the tender age of seven. Those who veered from the straight and narrow were dealt with severely: in the late eighteenth century a girl of seven was hanged in Norwich for stealing a petticoat.

The rise of the workhouse meant even harsher conditions for poor families, and many mothers, panic-stricken and desperate, simply abandoned their babies in the road or on the doorstep of wealthy homes, praying that the householder would show compassion and take them in. In 1719 Captain Thomas Coram, on his return to England from America, was so distressed at the sight of dead babies lying in the road that he began a long campaign, aiming for improved care for orphans and unmarried mothers. In 1739 he was awarded a Royal Charter and he went on to open the Foundling Hospital in London, of which the artist William Hogarth was a patron. Ninety babies a year were accepted but demand was far greater and watchmen were eventually employed at the doors to prevent mothers from abandoning infants when the hospital was full.

Life was certainly not easy for children growing up in eighteenth-century Britain, but this was the result of poverty rather than lack of sentiment. During the latter part of the century a degree of concern for the welfare of children developed that had been absent in previous centuries. With the approach of the nineteenth century the outlook for children began to look brighter as a decline in the belief of original sin helped to transform the popular image of children from corrupt and innately evil beings to angelic innocents.

5

'IF I SHOULD DIE ...'

– THE VICTORIAN MOTHER –

DURING THE NINETEENTH century medicine was finally able to offer real help to those in need of care, including women in childbirth. Unfortunately, partly due to Victorian attitudes to modesty, most women were unable to take full advantage of these medical advances, and the overall health of women remained poor. Childbirth remained a dangerous event and the perils faced by young mothers were echoed in literature of the time. The birth of Oliver Twist in the eponymous Dickens' novel brought about the death of his mother:

> The pale face of a young woman was raised feebly from the pillow; and a faint voice imperfectly articulated the words, 'Let me see the child, and die.' The nurse in attendance at the workhouse (an elderly woman) told the helpless surgeon, 'Lor bless her dear heart, when she has lived as long as I have, sir, and had thirteen children of her own, and all on 'em dead except two, and them in the workus with me, she'll know better than to take on in that way, bless her dear heart! Think what it is to be a mother, there's a dear young lamb, do.'

Many aspiring women were anxious to gain respect through meeting the new middle-class standards such as maintaining a scrupulously clean house and smart appearance, running themselves ragged in the process. Air vents were usually blocked to conserve heat and curtains were kept drawn during the day to prevent sun damage to furnishings.

Apart from the desire to portray a certain image by creating a perfect home, women were also desperate to achieve the perfect figure. Unfortunately for them, the fashionable shape during the nineteenth century required a tiny waist, ideally between fifteen and eighteen inches. Corsets were used to achieve these unnatural vital statistics, and women would lace themselves in so tightly that real physical damage would often result. The constrictions of the corset were thought to cause spinal abnormalities, tuberculosis, fainting and anal prolapse, as well as making childbirth much more hazardous.

> No one who has reflected upon the subject, and certainly no one who has a practical acquaintance with it, will contend that the annual deaths of 3,000 women in childbirth, and of 13,350 boys and 9,740 girls in the first month after delivery, or the suffering and deformity of those who escape with life, are natural and inevitable. Admit that the lives of a thousand, or even a hundred of those mothers could be saved and that many more might be rescued from injuries and pains which disable, or never leave them; and assuredly, no apathy, no false sentiment of delicacy, will prevent those who have the public health at heart from giving the subject the most attentive consideration.
> – From *The Magazine of Domestic Economy*, Vol. II, March 1844

Suggestions that so many of the difficulties that befell women could be avoided led to widespread concern for women's health. The general public became interested in the workings of the body, and those who could afford to began to follow the recommendations of the medical profession by developing healthy lifestyle habits comprising of a nutritious diet, fresh air, moderate exercise, unrestrictive clothing and personal hygiene.

> The mother is the most precious possession of the nation, so precious that society advances its highest well-being when it protects the functions of the mother.
>
> – Ellen Key (1849–1926)

Pregnancy

As a result of the dangers associated with childbirth, the prospect of excruciating pain and possible death, many mothers dreaded pregnancy. One of the most famous mothers who abhorred being pregnant was Queen Victoria. Her eldest daughter Vicky was equally unimpressed. She detested being pregnant, feeling ill and depressed each time.

Queen Victoria expressed sympathy to her daughter by letter in 1893: 'It is really too dreadful to have the first year of one's married life and happiness spoilt by discomfort and misery; I have a most lively recollection of what it was before you were born – fuss and precautions of all kinds and sorts.' The Princess and her mother corresponded by letter for forty years and died in the same year.

> Breathe not, hid Heart: cease silently,
> And though thy birth-hour beckons thee,
> Sleep the long sleep;
> The Doomsters heap
> Travails and teens around us here,
> And Time-wraiths turn our songsingings to fear.
>
> – Thomas Hardy, 'To an Unborn Pauper Child', 1897

As women gained greater knowledge about the workings of the human body and the world around them, their public voice grew in confidence and their anxieties were revealed. The large market in women's magazines helped to publicise the plight women faced during labour, and the perils of motherhood slowly gained greater prominence.

In response to these anxieties a number of books were published containing advice on diet, cravings, and how to cope with the discomforts of pregnancy, the first of which was *Hints to Mothers for the Management of Health During the Period of Pregnancy and in the Lying-in Room, with an Exposure of Popular Errors in Connection with those Subjects*, written by Thomas Bull in 1837. The book was hugely popular, reflecting how women were desperate to take control of their bodies and improve the health of both themselves and their children.

Once a woman suspected that she was pregnant she would seek medical attention, but physical examinations to ascertain pregnancy were shunned due to the constraints of modesty. For example, J. M. Jacquemier discovered in 1836 that pregnancy could be confirmed by examining the vagina; there would be a change in colour during early pregnancy. This test was regarded as highly indecent and was not mentioned again until the 1880s. Even the placing of a stethoscope on the abdomen of a pregnant women in order to check the fetal heartbeat was considered immoral.

> It is, perhaps, best upon the whole, that this great degree of modesty should exist even to the extent of putting a bar to researches, without which no very clear and understandable notions can be obtained of the sexual disorders. I confess I am proud to say that, in this country generally, certainly in my part of it, there are women who suffer the extremity of danger and pain rather than waive those scruples of delicacy which prevent their maladies from being fully exposed.
>
> – Charles D. Meigs, *Females and their Diseases*, 1848

Any decent, respectable practitioner would not have dreamed of ruining his reputation in such a manner. The vaginal speculum was widely used in France for ascertaining a pregnancy but it too was avoided in Britain due to the amount of exposure it involved. Doctors in Britain were among those who were disgusted by the use of such an immoral tool. In his book *On the Pathology and Treatment of Hysteria*, published in 1853, the physician Robert Brudenell Carter wrote:

> No one who has realised the amount of moral evil wrought in girls [...] whose prurient desires have been increased by Indian hemp and partially gratified by medical manipulation, can deny that the remedy is worse than the disease. I have [...] seen young unmarried women, of the middle class of society, reduced by the constant use of the speculum, to the mental and moral condition of prostitutes, seeking to give themselves the same indulgence by the practice of solitary vice, and asking every medical practitioner [...] to institute an examination of the sexual organs.

Fortunately, resistance to new equipment such as speculums, dilators and fetal sound monitors weakened as the century progressed. With such devices at their disposal obstetricians were able to improve the care not only of the mother, but also the unborn child. As the century progressed doctors were also able to offer some treatment for eclampsia: morphia, purgation, venesection (the opening of veins), and the administration of oxygen.

Birth Control

At the beginning of the nineteenth century there was a proliferation of written material about contraception available to the general public. As more and more people became aware of the subject, debates about it grew stronger. One of these publications was Richard Carlile's *Every Woman's Book*, published in 1826. Besides recommending certain methods of contraception such as *coitus interruptus*, the book claimed that French and Italian women used sponges that they 'wear fastened to their waists, and always have them at hand'.

> I trust you will agree with me in the hope that [...] the medical profession [...] must never identify itself in this matter [birth control] if this evil is to continue, it shall never exist as a sidewing of the healing art.
> – From *The Lancet*, 1873

Nevertheless, resistance to the distribution of birth control information was strong, particularly in America. Despite this, as more women gained positions of authority in society they began to speak out for their downtrodden sisters. Dr Elizabeth Blackwell, the first female American doctor, commented in 1870, 'I do not consider [...] that the object of marriage is to produce children.'

> There is an ill-founded notion current, that to reproduce an unlimited number of children is beneficial to society. It is only a benefit to children to be produced when they can be made to be healthy and happy.
> – Dr Elizabeth Blackwell, *How to Keep a Household in Health*, 1870

In Britain a large number of middle-class women were already practising birth control, appreciating a better standard of living with fewer children. Interestingly, a number of well-to-do women discovered that they could enjoy intercourse without the risk of pregnancy by employing the services of young men known as castratos, who were castrated at around the age of eight in order to keep their singing voices high.

The famous social activist Annie Besant worked tirelessly during the nineteenth century to bring knowledge of birth control to all women in the country. Following the arrest of a bookseller in Bristol for selling a book about contraception to members of the public, she embarked on a mission that would raise public awareness about birth control. Annie Besant and a colleague decided to publish the book, *The Fruits of Philosophy*, themselves.

This led to a very public trial, in which Annie Besant intended to prove that the book was not obscene. Initially they were convicted but the verdict was quashed on appeal, and she was successful in bringing matters of birth control to the forefront of public awareness.

Of course the trial and its associated publicity led to the sale of a huge number of copies of the notorious book, and numerous satirical poems were written about the affair, including the following anonymous ditty:

> [...] after the coup,
> All the ladies need do,
> Is to jump out of bed on the spot.
> Fill the squirt to the brim,
> Pump it well up to her quim;
> And the kid tickles into the pot.

As the century progressed a variety of methods of birth control became available. 'Gentlemen's nightcaps' (condoms) and sponges were particularly popular because they were easy to use. There were a number of different condom designs, one ingenious invention being a sort of vaginal tent made of eelskin, manufactured in America. In 1838 in Germany new cervical caps were designed, each individually moulded from the patient's cervix using wax. Wealthy women had their cap fashioned in ivory, gold or silver while those on a budget made do with latex. Although in use for many years, the cervical cap never became popular and was soon superseded by the Dutch cap, or diaphragm. This was a variation of the cervical cap, but it was a much larger rubber barrier that covered the entire vaginal wall. It was called 'Dutch' due to its popularity with early Dutch birth control clinics. Another birth control method was irrigation: the rinsing out of the vagina using a syringe, invented by the American physician Charles Knowlton.

Women would mix a concoction of alum, sulphate of zinc, sal eratus (bicarbonate of soda) and vinegar, then flush out the semen following every sexual encounter with their husbands.

Every Woman's Book contained a description of the irrigation method:

> The Irrigator is a kind of can, holding about two pints, which is hung on the wall by the woman's side of the bed, at the height of some four feet or more above the level of her head. This can has a long India rubber tube attached to a hole near its bottom, and at the mouthpiece end of the tube there is a little turn tap. Before getting into bed the woman fills the can with a solution of alum and water, as recommended above, places a bedpan and towel on a chair at the side of the bed; and after connection she has but to turn her back and slip the bedpan under her; then she inserts the mouth-piece of the India rubber tube into the vagina as far as possible, and the alum solution flows in and out again without causing wetting or trouble.

Not surprisingly, the irrigator did not gain widespread popularity.

Abortion

Despite the availability of contraception, abortion remained a major form of birth control. The English upper classes began to restrain pregnancy from around 1850, but the practice took longer to filter through to the lower classes. Death of the mother along with the fetus was a common consequence of abortion, but many women were prepared to risk their lives to free themselves from the prospect of continuing with their pregnancy.

During the nineteenth century many women turned to medical professionals for help with termination of their pregnancy; poorer women sought advice and treatment from midwives or herbalists, while those with the means to pay went to the doctor. Pills sold in the apothecary were often useless, based on laxatives, iron salts and alcohol. Rue, tansy, savin and culpeper were all popular and powerful abortifacients. Savin (a species of juniper) usually caused violent stomach pains, vomiting, severe headaches and sometimes even resulted in the agonising death of desperate women. Ely van der Warkle, an American obstetrician of the nineteenth century, took a dose of savin to find out for himself the intensity of the side effects:

> A violent pain in the abdomen, vomiting and powerful cathartic action, the tenesmus [the need to defecate], strangury [the need to urinate], heat and burning in the stomach, bowels, rectum and anal region; intoxication, flushed face, severe headache [...] salivation is often present. Its odour is clearly evident in the urine, which is increased in quantity and passed more frequently [...] distressing hiccup is very generally present.

One of the problems with administering powerful herbs was providing the correct dosage. It was difficult to establish the quality and strength of the individual plants and for how long they should be boiled. Some doses could cause convulsions and death, yet others did not even successfully abort the fetus.

Other equally grim methods were employed through most of the nineteenth century, such as the insertion of sharp instruments into the womb. Sharpened bamboo, meat skewers, knitting needles and crochets were all frequently used, the usual result being either perforation of the uterine wall or death from infection. The use of metal catheters finally did away with traditional barbaric practices, but it took many years for the method to become widespread.

There was no shortage of abortionists willing to 'help' women and, although illegal, advertisements were abundant and carefully worded, though thinly veiled, such as this from the *British Medical Journal* of 1868:

Mr —, Consulting Accoucher No —, after many years devoted to the practise of midwifery in its most intricate forms, is enabled to afford the immediate relief in all cases of female irregularity however difficult. Early applications preferred.

Superstition

The nineteenth century saw a great battle between science and superstition. Protestants had struggled for centuries to rid society of traditional ritualistic practices with little success. Although rituals were frowned upon by the Protestant Church, they at least gave people the feeling that they were taking action to protect themselves.

As scientists began to develop a greater understanding of themselves and the world around them, they realised the futility of adhering to ancient rituals. Curious old wives' tales still popular were that a sneeze during orgasm would prevent conception, and that a drink made from mistletoe would cure infertility (hence a kiss under the mistletoe).

It took a while longer for the knowledge gained in the field of science to have any benefit for the medical profession. Life, and particularly childbirth, remained as dangerous a journey as ever before and consequently people sought to protect themselves and their children by traditional means. Catholics, for example, had their own special method of protecting newborns. As far as they were concerned, birth was associated with nakedness, sin and shame, and many thought that a newborn baby arrived bathed in blood as a mark of the original sin of Eve, a symbol of the vileness of the human condition. Catholics would cross the baby after swaddling, sprinkle it with salt to keep it safe and place a coin in the cradle to drive the Devil away. When a baby was delivered the midwife would always lift it up in the air before putting it down in order to guarantee its 'rise in the world' and sometimes the baby's first drink would be cinder tea (water mixed with coal) to deter the Devil.

As soon as a woman realised she was pregnant she followed strict practices according to old beliefs and customs. With medical treatment being extremely limited and in most cases unavailable to the poorer communities, parents strived to avoid childhood illnesses by any means possible. Mothers were careful to avoid any upset, but unfortunately many of the old wives' tales persisted and new ones developed along the way. Things that were believed to be damaging to the unborn child were very difficult to dodge: birthmarks were considered to be the result of the sight of something frightening during pregnancy; harelips caused by the sight of a hare; and green eyes from seeing a snake.

Several beliefs involved the husband, one being that if he suffered sympathy pains, the greater his suffering, the more love he had for his wife.

Medical Progress

At the beginning of the nineteenth century without the ability to solve the three main problems of surgery – pain, infection and bleeding – doctors were unable to save the lives of many of their patients. However, following the Industrial Revolution doctors became armed with devices that enabled them to analyse and begin to control the causes of disease. Scientists initially used their new understanding of chemistry and physics to develop the engineering industries, but knowledge filtered through to the medical profession and enabled them to study how different chemicals could be used to cure ailments in the human body. Improvements in the production of microscopes in the nineteenth century furthered the understanding of disease, and engineers were able to improve the quality and design of surgical instruments.

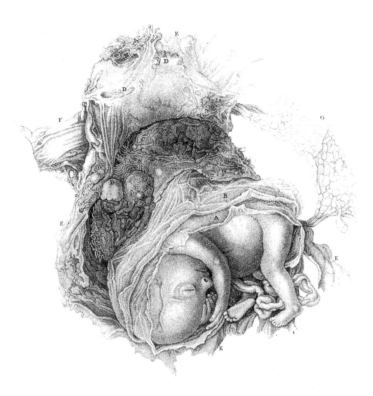

Nineteenth-century illustration of an opened ovum with a developed fetus

The Infection Crisis

As the general public became more aware of health issues and scientists continued to remove the veil of mystery shrouding the human body, many hoped that the dangers associated with childbirth would be greatly reduced. Unfortunately for women and their families, this hope was not to be realised until much later. The greatest obstacle to safe childbirth was puerperal fever, and this infection was not fully understood or competently tackled until the end of the century. Statistics reveal that there were few real improvements in the maternal mortality rate over the course of the century: in 1838 the maternal mortality rate was 5 in every 1,000 births and in 1892 the rate was 4.9 in every 1,000. The bacteria that caused puerperal fever was discovered in 1879, but doctors were reluctant to accept responsibility for the spread of the disease and were slow to adopt preventative measures to avoid it. Rubber gloves were finally introduced in 1890 by the American surgeon W. S. Halstead, and slowly other aseptic practices such as exposing dressings to steam and boiling instruments became more common.

During the nineteenth century it became increasingly popular for middle-class women to seek assistance from doctors during labour, but this only left them more at risk from developing infections. Doctors were not only more likely to intervene, but were also in contact with many other infectious diseases from other patients, and the vulnerability of women was increased. Despite recommendations by male midwives Charles White and Alexander Gordon, doctors refused to implement preventative measures. They resented the suggestion that they were often the cause of infections. It was a problem largely ignored until the mid-century when Oliver Wendell Holmes, an American doctor, and Ignaz Semmelweis, a Hungarian physician at the Vienna Lying-in Hospital, began to gain a greater understanding of the cause of puerperal fever.

The case of a doctor who had performed a post-mortem on a woman who had died of puerperal fever triggered Holmes's interest in investigating the transfer of infection. The doctor involved had attended several women after the post-mortem and then died shortly afterwards. All of the women he had attended contracted the fever. Holmes was convinced that the infection was spread by doctors in this way and pleaded with his colleagues to adopt preventative techniques. He urged all doctors involved in midwifery to avoid post-mortems and dissections, or at the very least ensure that they washed thoroughly, changed their clothes and then avoided contact with labouring women for a short period afterwards. Many of his colleagues were insulted and attacked his findings but Holmes was unapologetic: 'I take no offence and attempt no retort. No man can quarrel with me over the counterpane that covers a mother with the newborn infant at her breast.'

> The world has no such flower in any land,
> And no such pearl in any gulf in the sea,
> As any babe on any mother's knee.
>
> – Algernon Swinburne, 1866

Semmelweis arrived at the same conclusion following an incident at work in the Vienna Lying-in Hospital in 1839. Students at the hospital had lessons in the dissecting rooms, then went straight to the labour ward to attend women. The incidence of puerperal fever was extremely high but uninvestigated until a doctor was accidentally cut during a post-mortem. Septicaemia followed, and the doctor lost his life. Semmelweis drew parallels with women during delivery and was convinced that doctors' fingers were to blame for the transfer of 'cadaveric material' from dead bodies, which caused infections. His suggestions were ignored, and sadly he died of the very infection he was battling to defeat.

Despite warnings from men such as Holmes and Semmelweis, most doctors were so riddled with germs that hospitals remained the most dangerous of places to give birth. The conditions encountered by childbearing women in hospital were highlighted by surgeon Leon Le Fort in 1864 following a visit to the Paris Maternité:

> The principal ward contained a large number of beds in alcoves like English horse-stalls along each side. Ventilation was almost impossible. Floors and partitions were washed perhaps once a month [...] the ceilings had not been whitewashed for many a long year. Lying-in women who became ill were transferred to an isolation room regardless of the nature of the illness – puerperal fever cases and patients affected with diarrhoea, bronchitis, measles, or any other eruptive fever. Midwife pupils attend normal lying-in patients and fever cases alike, and perform all the necessary manipulations for every class of case.

The battle to gain control of infection was protracted and complicated. Bacteria had been spotted under a microscope as early as 1683 by Anton van Leeuwenhoek, yet the theory that bacteria was the result and not the cause of disease survived well into the nineteenth century. It was the work of Louis Pasteur in the 1860s that finally convinced the medical profession that microbes existed in the air and were often responsible for causing disease. Pasteur and others continued in their work and managed to identify haemolytic streptococcus, the bacteria that caused puerperal fever.

The surgeon Joseph Lister had read of Pasteur's work and devised a way of destroying the microbes by thorough cleansing using carbolic acid. The result was a dramatic reduction of the number of deaths through infection. The medical profession as a whole were slow to adopt aseptic techniques, but once widely practised the operating theatre and delivery room became much safer places.

The Caesarean Section

While circumstances for women in labour did not change drastically through most of the century, advances in the field of gynaecology paved the way for future improvements in obstetrics. Changes were desperately needed. The Caesarean, for example, had been used for many centuries as a last resort in difficult labours, but the problems that caused the operation to be so dangerous remained during the early nineteenth century. The discovery of effective methods of anaesthesia obviously reduced the shock of the operation but initially did little to reduce mortality statistics. In 1849 Dr Radford of Manchester reported that he had lost three mothers and babies out of five attempts with the use of anaesthetics, although in 1900 Dr Sinclair from the same medical centre reported ten out of ten successes.

In an effort to improve the often dire results of Caesareans, pioneers around the world worked to refine gynaecological techniques. One of the first breakthroughs came when the American gynaecologist James Marion Sims managed to repair a vesico-vaginal fistula (tear between the bladder and vagina), which is usually caused by very protracted and difficult labour. As a result of his success he moved to New York and opened the first hospital dedicated to curing the diseases suffered by women. Knowledge and expertise grew from these small beginnings, and by the end of the century hysterectomies could be carried out and ectopic pregnancies dealt with reasonably efficiently.

Once surgeons realised that the uterine wall should be stitched up following surgery, the Caesarean section became much safer for women. Until the 1870s the Caesarean technique had remained basically the same over the centuries. Doctors thought that the uterine wall would repair itself and consequently many women simply bled to death. In 1876 the Italian surgeon Eduardo Porro found that women were more likely to survive the Caesarean if a hysterectomy was performed at the same time, reducing the risk of sepsis and haemorrhage. Fortunately a less drastic procedure was followed by the surgeon Robert Lawson Tait in England during gynaecological operations; the suturing (stitching) of the uterine wall. Shortly after his successes in this field were reported, the Germans Ferdinand Kehrer and Max Sanger used the technique after Caesareans, with astonishing results. When combined with aseptic techniques the mortality rate following section fell from 65–75 per cent to 5–10 per cent.

Pain Relief in Labour

Although Caesareans remained dangerous and the practice of craniotomy continued, there were improvements in the design of forceps and other obstetrical instruments. The ancient art of version was also improved by John Braxton Hicks during the 1860s. Braxton Hicks discovered that the technique was much more successful when combined with external manipulation to alter the position of a malpresented baby. It was also Braxton Hicks who first realised that women experience regular 'practice' contractions throughout pregnancy (when modern women rush to hospital in false labour they are told they are experiencing Braxton Hicks contractions).

With the production of more precise surgical instruments following the industrial revolution, surgeons were able to increase the speed of operations, but one of the biggest problems – pain – continued to shock and kill many patients. The prospect of enduring an operation without anaesthesia was appalling, and consequently patients had to be dragged into the theatre, screaming piteously, and held down with leather straps before surgery could begin.

Many scientists performed experiments with various chemicals in an attempt to find a safe and more effective pain reliever than opium, the first of which were nitrous oxide (laughing gas) and ether. Ether was found to irritate the lungs but another substance quickly gained popularity: chloroform. In 1847 the obstetrician James Young Simpson from Edinburgh decided to test the effectiveness of this new drug and quickly passed out. He became a great advocate of its use to aid women in labour.

> Nothing begins and nothing ends
> That is not paid with moan;
> For we are born in other's pain
> And perish in our own.
>
> – Francis Thompson (1859–1907)

This was strongly criticised by the clergy, as it was still thought to be against God's will to ease a woman's pain during labour. Men reasoned that to suffer pain was feminine; it demonstrated their weakness and inferiority to the male sex. Many asserted that the pain of labour was grossly overestimated anyway; one popular stereotype had it that Native American women sought no special attention during pregnancy and worked until the onset of labour when they would give birth alone and resume tasks immediately afterwards. Some men agreed with the author George H. Napheys who wrote that Western women had become 'sexually aggressive, intellectually ambitious and defective in proper womanly submission and selflessness', and who believed that if women returned to a more subordinate and less selfish role they would no longer suffer during childbirth. Women remained unconvinced, however, and while many remained reluctant to submit to new medical innovations most were eager to use chloroform during labour. It was no longer an acceptable concept to endure pain and suffering in return for eternal blessings. The idea that God had either died or totally withdrawn Himself from the world was gaining popularity among scientists, and many began to feel that salvation could only be achieved through human efforts rather than divine intervention.

James Young Simpson was convinced that 'if the object of the medical practitioner is really twofold as it has always, until of late been declared to be, viz: "the alleviation of human suffering and the preservation of human life" then it is our duty, as well as our privilege, to use all legitimate means to mitigate and remove the physical sufferings of the mother during parturition'. Many in the medical profession opposed him, believing that to avoid pain was cowardly and showed that Satan was at work in the world. Simpson replied to his critics by arguing that God obviously agreed with pain relief as he had caused Adam to fall into a deep sleep in the Garden of Eden in order to remove one of his ribs.

In America many doctors were equally opposed to the use of pain relief on moral, religious and emotional grounds. The Philadelphian Dr Charles Meigs believed that if a woman felt no pain during labour she would feel less love for the infant she delivered. He reasoned that the severe suffering experienced during labour produced strong emotional attachments between mother and child; mothers would do anything to protect their infant, having tolerated so much agony to bring them into the world.

It was thanks to Queen Victoria herself that pain relief in labour finally became widely accepted. When she first married, the Queen was happy except for her one dread – pregnancy. Her fears seem to have been justified following the birth of her first daughter in 1841. In a letter to her uncle King Leopold I of Belgium, she wrote: 'Men never, at least seldom, think what a hard task it is for us women to go through this very often.' With each pregnancy she felt low and depressed, dreading the ordeal that lay before her, and she wrote following the birth of the Prince of Wales: 'My sufferings were really severe, and I don't know what I should have done, but for the great comfort and support my beloved Albert was to me.' She was therefore thrilled when Dr John Snow administered 'that blessed chloroform' during the birth of her eighth child. The Queen wrote: 'The effect was soothing, quieting and delightful beyond measure.' With such approval from the Queen of England the clergy dared not campaign against its use.

Sadly, for some women, the effectiveness of chloroform became a double-edged sword. Although many welcomed its use with utter relief, others suffered at the hands of impatient birth attendants. In cases where the cervix was slow to dilate or if the placenta was obstructing delivery, the cervix would sometimes be forcibly dilated or even sliced open to make way for the baby's head. Of course any woman subjected to such treatment died from haemorrhage and infection, and as a result mortality figures rose dramatically. As the century came to a close these practices were eradicated, once the Caesarean section became a viable option.

Newborn

Abstractedly, I have no tendre for them till they have become a little human; an ugly baby is a very nasty object – and the prettiest is frightful when undressed – till about four months; in short, as long as they have their big body and little limbs and that terrible frog-like action.
– Queen Victoria in a letter to her daughter Princess Vicky, the Princess Royal, 2 May 1859

Queen Victoria wrote a letter to her daughter Princess Vicky in 1863 announcing the birth of a new baby to their dear friend Princess Marie of Prussia at Osborne House. The details provide a colourful picture of the fear that accompanied childbirth, and the relief felt once the baby was safely delivered, not only by the mother, but also those surrounding her:

> Oh! dear child, thank God! darling Marie is safe with her magnificent baby but it was an awful labour – 48 hours in pain and 18 in constant labour! And at last at two in the morning of Friday […] Dr Farre said she must not be allowed to go on or she would be exhausted and the child would die and so instruments must be used!! Poor Ernest was in despair and crying – and so I sat by her and they put her completely under chloroform and she was like as if she slept, I stroking her face all the time and while Dr Farre most skilfully and cleverly delivered her without her knowing or feeling anything, and only woke when she heard the child cry.

Babies of wealthy parents were often viewed as a blessing and a rich reward. Many church sermons welcomed the fruit of the womb into the congregation as a gift from God and 'pledge of love' between husband and wife. Women in poorer families, however, could not think of their babies in quite the same way as those adoring mothers who only spent an hour or so a day with them. Well-educated mothers with a nanny and fully equipped nursery could agree with writer Martin F. Tupper that 'a babe in the house is as a well-spring of pleasure'. Those in poorer circumstances often had a different perspective. A woman with few female friends or relatives could expect little or no domestic help, and certainly none from her husband.

In *Sybil*, Benjamin Disraeli, whose popular political novels often reflected an interest in social reform, wrote of a poor mother who had to use the services of an old woman to care for her newborn:

About a fortnight after his mother had introduced him into the world, she returned to her factory, and put her infant out to nurse – that is to say, paid threepence a week to an old woman, who takes charge of these new-born babes for the day, and gives them back at night to their mothers, as they hurriedly return from the scene of their labour to the dungeon or den, which is still by courtesy called 'home'. The expense is not great: laudanum and treacle, administered in the shape of some popular elixir, affords these innocents a brief taste of the sweets of existence, and, keeping them quiet, prepares them for the silence of their impending grave. Infanticide is practised as extensively and as legally in England, as it is on the banks of the Ganges.

> Of all the joys that lighten suffering earth,
> what joy is welcomed like a new born child.
> – Caroline Norton (1808–1877)

Innovations in Childcare

For most of human history, parents managed without special transport for their babies. Sometimes a sling or papoose was used in traditional societies to reduce the strain on backs and arms, but the use of slings would have been unthinkable in the West due to the impractical dresses women wore and the 'hands off' approach of many mothers. Tired mothers and nurses often resorted to various wheeled vehicles in order to rest their aching limbs a while. Stick or spindle wagons, of the type used by hop-pickers, were often adapted and used for the carriage of little children.

For the children of nobility no expense was spared; rich parents had luxury miniature carriages made for their children, which would be pulled by an animal such as a goat, pony or dog. The earliest known surviving baby carriage in England was made for the children of the third Duke of Devonshire, designed by William Kent in 1730. It was a scaled down version of a contemporary

*Nineteenth-century painting of a Victorian mother and child by Sir
Lawrence Alma-Tadema*

carriage, made in the shape of a scallop shell, of elaborate and ornate construction. This idea gradually filtered down to the middle classes who designed far simpler carts that parents could pull themselves. In the early nineteenth century the design changed and they were pushed, not pulled, enabling the carer to see the baby while walking.

My aged friend, Miss Wilkinson,
Whose mother was a Lambe,
Saw Wordsworth once, and Coleridge, too.
One morning in her pram.
This was a three-wheeled vehicle,
Of iron and of wood,
It had a leather apron,
But it hadn't any hood.

– Walter de la Mare, 'The Bards'

These early prams, modelled on postmen's delivery carts, were known as 'mailcarts'. Others, which were basically cradles on wheels, were known as 'bassinets'. The first factory specialising in carriages for children opened in 1840. The carriages were designed with three wheels until 1875 due to a law banning four-wheeled vehicles from footpaths. They became known as perambulators ('walkers').

Such vehicles soon became extremely popular and business flourished for the pram-makers. By the end of the 1860s there were at least thirty pram-makers in London. The 1860 *Dictionary of Daily Wants*, which contained information on all matters of practical and domestic utility, declared the perambulator to be 'one of the most useful inventions of the day', but warned against overuse:

The great advantage of the perambulator is that it permits children to be out in the open without subjecting the nurse to any fatigue. It is as well, however, to lift the child out occasionally and to allow them to exercise their limbs until they feel tired, when they can be placed in the perambulator again. In cold weather this is especially necessary as children being subjected to the exposure of the keen air in a state of inactivity are liable to be affected with cramp, rheumatism and other painful affections.

The Dictionary of Daily Wants also expressed concern that nursemaids would 'wheel their young charges to a certain spot, and leave them sitting in their prams by the hour together, so that they may be spared the trouble of looking after them, and enjoy their gossip uninterrupted'. It was suggested that mothers should follow their nannies to the park to check that their infants were not being ignored. Marion Harland's 1886 *Common Sense in the Nursery* even suggested to mothers to 'take an early breakfast yourself, and arrayed in lawn, percale or modest gingham, brave public opinion by tending to your darling in person. To wheel a perambulator is a crucial test of your moral courage and innate ladyhood'.

Apart from prams one of the best inventions to arise during the nineteenth century was the nappy. Towelling material appeared in the late 1800s, and was welcomed with joy and relief. Safety pins were invented in 1878; until then nappies or 'tail-clouts' were made of plain linen with a 'pilch' or thick flannel cloth for extra protection at night. During the eighteenth century an oiled piece of silk was worn over the pilch as a waterproof cover to contain the 'disagreeables' as the nappy contents were politely referred to. Pins were used to hold nappies together and often stuck into the baby's skin. Sometimes a mother or nurse would attempt to comfort a crying baby or toddler with heavy-handed patting, driving the pins further into the flesh.

Keeping babies amused and avoiding boredom has been the objective of parents through the ages, and from early on it was found that the most simple items could amuse infants for hours; in 1826 the German educational reformer Friedrich Froebel recommended that an ideal way to occupy a resting baby was a bird in a cage. Rattles have always been popular both to occupy babies and to help them to cut their first teeth. Eighteenth- and early-nineteenth-century rattles were often made of gold or silver with a strip of coral or bone for the baby to bite on.

> Through the house what busy joy,
> Just because the infant boy
> Has a tiny tooth to show.
> I have got a double row,
> All as white, and all as small;
> Yet no one cares for mine at all.
> He can say but half a word,
> Yet that single sound's preferred
> To all the words that I can say
> In the longest summer day.
> He cannot walk, yet if he put
> With mimic motion out his foot,
> As if he thought he were advancing,
> It's prized more than my best dancing.
>
> – Mary Lamb, 'The First Tooth', 1809

Nursing

The painter Benjamin Haydon suffered the loss of his daughter, Fanny, when she was just two years old:

The life of this child has been one continued torture. She was weaned at three months from her mother's weakness, and attempted to be brought up by hand. This failed, and she was reduced to a perfect skeleton. One day when I was kissing her, she sucked my cheek violently. I said, 'This child wants the bosom even now'. Our medical friend said it was an experiment, but we might try it. I got a wet nurse instantly, and she seized the bosom like a tigress; in a few months she recovered, but the woman who came to suckle her weaned her own child.

I called on the nurse before she came, and found a fine baby, her husband and herself in great poverty. I said, 'What do you do with this child?' She replied, 'Wean it sir. We must do so, we are poor!' I went away. 'Is it just,' thought, I 'to risk the life of another child to save my own?' I went home in tortured feelings of what to do, but a desire to save my own predominated.

The nurse came, Fanny was saved, but the fine baby of the poor nurse paid the penalty. I was never easy. 'Fanny never can and never will prosper,' I imagined. What right had I to take advantage of the poverty of this poor woman to save my own child, when I found out she had an infant? I ought not to have had her. In spite of my reason I did have her and though my own child was saved for the time, I always felt it would be but justice if my child too in the end became the sacrifice to the Manes of the child which had died in consequence of its mother leaving it.

In spite of the employment of a wet nurse Fanny later died, as did the child of the wet nurse, who was forced to be weaned too early.

There have been many different theories as to how and what to feed a tiny baby, concoctions usually including boiled water, bread, cereals and sugar. In 1857 the journal *British Pharmacopoeia* suggested that a passable alternative to mother's or cow's milk could be made by boiling vineyard snails with pearl barley. Small wonder that until the late nineteenth century a baby's survival was largely a matter of chance!

> Disease and death are the usual consequences of the present erroneous method of bringing up children by hand. Scarcely one out of four of these little innocents live to get over the cutting of their teeth.
>
> – From *The Female Instructor* or *Young Woman's Companion*, 1815

Fresh milk was critical to the success of hand-feeding, but it was very difficult to obtain, and dairymen would often cheat by diluting the milk with water to make it go further, adding chalk to give it a creamy colour. It was then put into unwashed containers and delivered in warm weather. Although Louis Pasteur had discovered the process of pasteurisation in the 1860s, it was still common for unpasteurised milk to be sold from the churn in England until the 1920s.

> Upon her soothing breast
> She lulled her little child;
> A winter sunset in the west,
> A dreary glory smiled.
>
> – Emily Brontë, 'Upon her Soothing Breast', 1839

Although breast-feeding was encouraged by the medical profession, the process was still not completely understood. It was believed that colostrum, the substance secreted from the breasts in the first couple of days following birth (now known to be extremely beneficial to the newborn) was indigestible and possibly harmful.

Many women continued to find breast-feeding too unpalatable to contemplate. The novelist Anthony Trollope noted in *Dr Thorne*, published in 1858, 'Of course Lady Arabella could not suckle the young heir herself. Ladies Arabella never can. They are gifted with the powers of being mothers, but not nursing mothers. Nature gives them bosoms for show but not for use!'

Victorian newspapers displayed a number of advertisements offering 'good breast milk'. When a wet nurse applied for a position of employment she would be subjected to a rigorous examination: teeth, gums, throat, skin and hair would be inspected, and her breasts would have to be firm, not fat or flabby, with erect and firm nipples. The milk would have to be bluish white with a sweet taste and she should have high morals and a calm temperament.

Those mothers who did attempt to breast-feed their babies often encountered difficulties due to flat nipples. Stays and corsets, which were so popular during the eighteenth and nineteenth centuries, forced the breasts upwards to such an extent that nipples would flatten to the point of inversion. In 1857 Dr John Walsh, in his *Manual of Domestic Economy*, complained that, 'in the present state of society, from the pressure of stays carried through several generations, the

Nineteenth-century etching of a mother breast-feeding her child

nipples are so shortened and injured in their development that, if left to itself, many a child would actually starve'.

Nipple shields were often used as a remedy and were worn both night and day. Designed to fit over the breast, the shields had small holes in the nipple area, which encouraged inverted nipples outwards as the baby sucked. Poorer women made do with hollowed-out nutmeg or walnut shells.

Made in a variety of materials including pewter, bone, glass, horn, ivory and silver, nipple shields enabled even a mother suffering the agony of ulcerated nipples to continue feeding her baby, and, since infants were often fed until their third year, nipple shields offered protection against overenthusiastic toddlers. *The English Woman's Domestic Magazine* of 1859 was firm in its conviction that late weaning from the breast was inappropriate: 'Nature never ordained a child to live on suction after having endowed it with teeth to bite and to grind, and nothing is more out of place and unseemly than to hear a child with a set of twenty teeth ask for the breast.'

> What you say of the pride of giving life to an immortal soul is very fine, dear, but I own I cannot enter into that, I think much more of our being like a cow or dog at such moments; when our poor nature becomes so very animal and unecstatic – but for you dear, if you are sensible and reasonable, not in ecstacy nor spending your day with nurses and wet nurses, which is the ruin of many a refined and intellectual young lady …
> – Queen Victoria in a letter to her daughter Princess Vicky, the Princess Royal, 15 June 1858

The desire to breast-feed is said to be closely associated with one's family's opinion of it: if a mother has been breast-fed herself she is far more likely to breast-feed her own baby. Queen Victoria is a famous example of an exception to this. To everyone's astonishment, Queen Victoria's mother, the Duchess of Kent, had fed Victoria herself, choosing not to engage the customary wet nurse, because she adored Victoria so much she could not bear to think of another woman being so close to her. Despite this, Queen Victoria was shocked when some of her own daughters and granddaughters insisted on feeding their babies themselves.

> The thrilling sensations that accompany the act of giving suck can be conceived only by those who have felt them, while the mental raptures of a fond mother at such moments are far beyond the powers of description or fancy.
> – Dr William Buchan, *Advice to Mothers*, 1803

Churchmen of all denominations made attempts to encourage women to breast-feed their own babies and quoted Genesis 21: 'and she [Sarah] said, "Who would have said unto Abraham, that Sarah should have given children suck? For I have borne him a son in his old age."' This passage shows that Sarah had not been too proud to suckle Isaac.

Puritans believed that suckling one's own infant was a mother's sacred duty, a godly responsibility and a sign of maternal devotion. Indeed, so proud was one Benjamin Brand of his wife's maternal dedication that he had recorded on her tombstone in 1836 that she bore him twelve children 'all nursed with her unborrowed milk'.

> For the next 8 or 10 months, Oliver was the victim of a coarse treachery and deception – he was brought up by hand.
> – Charles Dickens, *Oliver Twist*, 1838

It is a great pity that breast-feeding raised such feelings of repulsion during a time when contraception was both controversial and difficult to obtain. During lactation a woman's fertility is severely diminished, and although it is still possible to become pregnant, it is unlikely. Women, desperate to limit the number of pregnancies they had to endure, could have achieved this by breast-feeding.

> So for the mother's sake the child was dear,
> And dearer was the mother for the child.
> — Samuel Taylor Coleridge (1772–1834)

Life After Birth

During the early part of the nineteenth century almost all babies were carried around wrapped in a shawl and cap or bonnet. The bonnet was worn during the daytime and at night, both indoors and out. 'Chills' were to be avoided at all costs. Mrs Beeton, in her *Book of Household Management*, first published 1861, insisted that 'the infant during the first month must not be exposed to strong light, or much air; and in carrying it about the passages, stairs [...] the nurse should always have its head-flannel on, to protect the eyes and ears from the currents of air'.

The tradition of pink for a girl and blue for a boy did not become popular until the late nineteenth century, and until this time it was often difficult to distinguish boy babies from girls, although some mothers would sew a satin ribbon on the left side of a bonnet for a boy and in front for a girl.

From birth, babies were swathed in ostentatiously long 'quasi-adult' clothes, and both boys and girls were dressed in pantaloons and stiff skirts covered in frills. White dresses were worn by both sexes until age three or four in the seventeenth century and five or six in the eighteenth century. These were replaced by stiff dresses in plaid wool or velvet in the 1840s or 1850s. A boy would then take the symbolic step out of ankle length frocks into breeches while a girl would continue to dress like her mother.

Artist Ford Madox Brown's 1847 religious work entitled
Our Lady of Good Children

> Children, you are very little,
> And your bones are very brittle,
> If you would grow great and stately,
> You must learn to walk sedately.
>   – Robert Louis Stevenson, *A Child's Garden of Verses*, 1885

Once they were no longer babes in arms, Victorian toddlers were often dressed inappropriately in the name of fashion, and some suffered from the cold as their dresses often left their necks and shoulders exposed. Appearance, particularly amongst the upper classes, was of the utmost importance, with comfort barely even considered. Girls often suffered as their mothers did in the name of beauty, squeezed into tiny muslin dresses tied tightly around the waist. Thankfully, the appearance of the perambulator boosted the fashion for warm woollen clothing. The Rational Dress Society of 1881 advocated the use of soft wool for babies and young children and suggested that all layettes (complete sets of baby clothes and accessories) should include '4 woollen binders, 4 woollen vests, 4 flannel or cashmere robes and 48 Turkish towelling nappies'.

> Children begin by loving their parents,
> after a time they judge them.
> Rarely, if ever, do they forgive them.
>   – Oscar Wilde (1854–1900)

Good deportment was considered to be of the utmost importance, and most children of the upper classes were strapped to various contraptions to promote good posture. Deportment chairs were used to keep children's backs straight. These were uncomfortable to sit on, with high legs and tiny seats, but the children who sat in these chairs during lessons were the fortunate ones. Some children were strapped to a backboard and had to do their lessons standing up. As the day wore on they would become exhausted but were prevented from slouching by strategically placed spikes on the board. As a child Katherine Caroline Cavendish, the future Duchess of Westminster, was forced to wear a backboard with a violin string tied tightly around her shoulders: if she slouched the string would cut into her flesh. In some cases small bones were broken and reset, without anaesthetic, in an attempt to improve a child's posture.

> Is it not a fundamental error in Christians to consider children as innocent beings, rather than as beings who bring into the world a corrupt nature and evil disposition which it should be the great aim of education to rectify?
>
> – Hannah More, *Strictures*, Vol. 5, 1808

The Victorians had many devices at their disposal to control not only children's shape and posture, but also their character. Humiliating contraptions such as dunce hats, placards and finger stocks, which immobilised the child's hands behind their back, were regularly used in Victorian Dames' Schools. Finger stocks were also used by mothers on very young infants to prevent and punish masturbation. This habit was greatly feared and was one which Ada Ballin, in her 1902 book *From Cradle to School, A Book for Mothers*, advised 'must always be looked for in little children, especially in little girls in the early years of life'. Hands, knees and feet of young children were often tightly strapped in an effort to prevent exploration and preserve the child's soul.

Children were simply treated as small-scale adults, and the children of poor families were expected to work if they wanted to be fed. In fact, children were so undervalued by society that it only became an offence to steal a baby from its parents in 1814, although before this time, it was illegal to steal the clothes they were dressed in.

> One cannot love lumps of flesh, and little infants are nothing more.
> – Lord Byron (1788–1824)

As the century progressed, however, the lives of children began to change for the better. Society slowly began to realise that children had their own ways of thinking, feeling, and doing, and parents tried to construct childhood as a privileged state of being. Reformers such as Lord Shaftesbury and Dr Thomas Barnardo were partly responsible for the increased affection towards children, but interestingly enough, it was the growing emergence of children's books that finally swayed public opinion with regard to child welfare. Until the appearance of tiny tracts such as *Bob the Cabin Boy* in the eighteenth century books written especially for children were scarce. The only book with stories they could enjoy was the Bible. If they wanted something easier to read they could share their parents' chapbooks, which were pamphlets similar to our comics or magazines.

By the second half of the eighteenth century a distinct children's literature had emerged which blossomed in the nineteenth century. Charles Kingsley's *The Water Babies*, Thomas Hughes' *Tom Brown's Schooldays*, and the writings of the Brothers Grimm, Hans Christian Andersen and Lewis Carroll did much to interest the public in the sufferings and feelings of children.

Charles Darwin's theory of evolution (that humans gradually evolved from animals, rather than being direct descendants of Adam and Eve) also helped; as his views gained wider acceptance, the idea of children being tainted by original sin lost popularity. Children had been raised in line with biblical principles such as Proverbs 29:15: 'The rod and reproof give wisdom; but a child left to himself brings his mother to shame.' As Darwin's views gained wider acceptance, severe punishments perpetrated as a means of saving a child's soul no longer seemed justified or necessary.

The softening public mood was echoed by publications such as *The Ladies' Magazine* of June 1833, which described childhood as, 'a state which speaks to us of Heaven, which tells us of those pure angelic beings which surround the throne of God, untouched by sin, untainted by the breath of corruption'.

As interest in the welfare of children increased, action was taken to put an end to their misuse and abuse. The Chimney Sweepers Act was passed in 1864, finally ending the gross ill-usage of boys as chimney sweeps and the Society for the Prevention of Cruelty to Children was founded in 1884.

> I don't know what Scrope Davies meant by telling you I liked children, I abominate the sight of them so much that I have always had the greatest respect for the character of Herod.
> – Lord Byron in a letter dated 30 August, 1811

Gradually children in Britain gained more leisure time and were able to spend carefree hours playing. Since the nineteenth century toys have been manufactured in increasing numbers, with the only major decline occurring during the world wars. From ancient Egyptian times to the present day, dolls have been one of the most popular toys of all. In fact, dolls were among the very first toys ever made. Greek and Roman dolls had bodies made from wood or clay, sometimes with jointed limbs. Toy manufacturers began to make dolls in large numbers in the eighteenth century. As time progressed dolls with closing eyes, baby dolls that drank from a bottle, and talking dolls began to appear.

In the eighteenth and nineteenth centuries paper was widely used in toy-making. The most common paper toys were printed shapes on cut-out sheets. Children could stick these on to stiff card, cut them out and join them together to make a finished toy. Theatres, complete with scenery and actors, ships, and dolls supplied with a change of paper clothes were all popular. Ironically, toys like these made by the children themselves probably provided many more hours of entertainment than the expensive mass-produced toys of today, and had the added benefit of stimulating the child's imagination and encouraging story-telling skills.

Victorian parents believed that toys should teach and amuse at the same time, and many of the toys produced during the late Victorian period were 'educational', such as building blocks decorated with letters, and jigsaw puzzles with themes from the Bible. Dolls' houses were considered very useful toys for girls as they could learn how to manage a household efficiently. Board games were used to teach good behaviour, one such being entitled 'Virtue Rewarded and Vice Punished'!

As the nineteenth century progressed, many came to realise that the way a child was treated was crucial in determining what sort of adult they would become. Education was valued, and there was growing interest in the way young children learn. Childhood began to be idealised as the best stage of life, a time of innocence and joy. Children were at last able to take time to play, smoothing their path from infancy to adulthood.

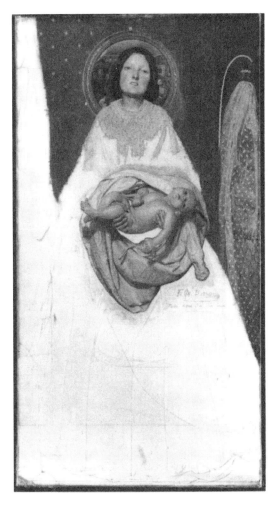

Victorian mother and child in Madonna-like pose

6

THE SWEETNESS OF LIFE:

– TWENTIETH-CENTURY BIRTH –

AS THE NINETEENTH century came to a close, real concern for the health and welfare of mothers and their babies had begun. The increasingly influential women's pressure groups, including the Women's Labour League and the Women's Co-operative Guild, had at last succeeded in gaining attention from politicians, and efforts began to reduce maternal and infant mortality rates. In America feminist and suffragette groups pushed unremittingly for improvements in the care of women in childbirth, focusing on the issue of pain relief.

There were still many problems to be solved but at least there was a general consensus that things had to change. Until this time women knew that once they were married their lives would be dominated by the process of labour and birth with little reprieve. They had minimal control over their fertility and must have entered each labour wondering if they would be fortunate enough to survive.

The Gradual Acceptance of Birth Control
Progress on the distribution of contraceptive advice remained slow. Established churches continued to object to its use and claimed that materialism was at the heart of the motivation to control

fertility. Annie Besant, the leading campaigner and advocate of birth control, was a well-known atheist, which must have further antagonised members of the clergy.

Gradually, however, things began to change, and the use of contraception was reflected in the declining birth rate. Officially the clergy was opposed to contraception, yet the results of a 1905 Fabian Society investigation into the falling birth rate showed the highest decline among the middle and upper classes, notably among doctors and the clergy. It was concluded, after two year's deliberation, that, 'the decline in the birth rate is principally, if not entirely, the result of deliberate volition in the regulation of the married state'. In other words, married couples must be practising birth control of some sort – a logical conclusion! While the medical profession were slow to accept birth control as routine practice, clearly they were not averse to limiting their own family size; it was only the disadvantaged who were missing out on the benefits of a smaller family.

The public mood was undoubtedly swaying gently towards the understanding that fewer children who were able to enjoy the benefits of greater prosperity was preferable to having a large family, destined to live in poor and cramped conditions. Some doctors added their voices to those who argued that children's standard of health could be improved if fewer were actually born. Others felt that the argument was really about survival of the fittest and found the whole idea abhorrent.

> Apart from the pressure of population, it is time to be learning: 1) That annual childbearing is still common, is cruelly exhaustive to maternal life, and this often in actual duration as well as quality; 2) That it is similarly injurious to the standard of offspring; and hence 3) That an interval of two years between births (some gynaecologists go so far as three) is due alike to mother and offspring.
> – Sidney Webb, *The Decline in the Birth Rate*, 1907

For most of history intercourse has been seen as a vehicle to achieve procreation. To limit the number of children born was, for some, to ignore God's instruction to 'go forth and multiply', and the notion of having sexual intercourse merely for pleasure was still considered immoral. The majority of medical opinion was opposed – in public at least – to birth control during the early part of the twentieth century. The following extract from a letter sent to the *British Medical Journal* by a female gynaecologist is typical:

> The people and nations who practice artificial prevention of conception and who therefore have no restraint in their sexual passions are likely to become effeminate and degenerate. The removal of the sanction of matrimony and the unhindered and unbalanced sexual indulgence that would follow would war against self-control, chivalry and self-respect.

Despite reservations in certain conservative sectors of society, women were becoming increasingly encouraged to limit the size of their families. As their circumstances improved and better healthcare became more widely available, women saw a future that included activities outside the home, and they saw contraception as an aid to achieving this. Moreover, improved hygiene and healthcare meant that fewer babies were losing their lives; consequently parents no longer had to bear many children in order to guarantee the survival of a few.

In 1918 Marie Stopes decided to take full advantage of the public's softening mood towards contraception, publishing *Married Love*, one of the UK's first sex manuals, and a supplement concerning family planning, *Wise Parenthood: A Book for Married People*. Born in Edinburgh in 1880, Marie Stopes had graduated from University College London with a double first in botany and geology and went on to get a doctorate in Munich. Stopes had been driven to write on the subject of sex as a result of difficulties experienced in her first marriage. She knew there was a problem with her first husband but in her innocence she did not realise exactly what was wrong. After investigating the problem by reading medical texts in the British Library, she realised that her husband was impotent and she was still a virgin. Her first book opened with these words:

> In my first marriage I paid such a terrible price for sex-ignorance that I feel that knowledge gained at such a cost should be placed at the service of humanity [...] I hope this book will save some others years of heartache and blind questioning in the dark.

The book was written in flowery language, and, although a bestseller, many found it incompatible with the reality of their everyday lives. 'Welling up in her are the wonderful tides, scented and enriched by the myriad experience of the human race from its ancient days of leisure and flower-wreathed lovemaking.'

Throughout the country modesty still prevailed, and the open discussion of sexual matters in such circumstances was a daunting task. Marie Stopes' book was labelled immoral and obscene by religious leaders, the medical profession and the press, but the general public loved it. Her claim that women should enjoy sex as much as men was a revolutionary idea and shocking for the establishment.

Marie Stopes was determined to educate all women about the value of birth control, including the very poor and illiterate, as she felt these women would benefit the most from her knowledge. In 1921 Marie Stopes and her second husband opened a clinic in London where free advice and contraceptives, including sponges, caps and suppositories, were made available to everyone.

In response to increasing demand more clinics were opened around the country. Marie went on to found the Society for Constructive Birth Control and worked with other birth control societies to form a national birth control organisation, the National Birth Control Council, now known as the Family Planning Association.

Now Marie Stopes International provides services in 28 countries around the world, their mission being to 'ensure the fundamental human right of all people to have children by choice, not chance'. Apart from contraceptive and abortion advice, specialist centres around Britain offer vasectomy and female sterilisation services, infertility investigations, pre-conception screenings, and psychosexual and post-abortion counselling. In 1999 Marie Stopes was voted 'Woman of the Millennium' by the *Guardian* newspaper's readers.

While those involved in matters of contraception were making progress in Britain, great battles were being fought by other reformers around the world, desperate to bring knowledge and choice to women everywhere. Despite the work of campaigners in France, a ruling by the Government classed contraception with abortion in 1920, and all matters concerning birth control became illegal. In America Margaret Sanger worked tirelessly for birth control despite enormous opposition. She fought against ignorance, prejudice, religious tenets and the law. Part of the driving force behind her mission was the death of her mother at forty-nine. Sanger felt that her mother died at this young age as a result of the strain of enduring eighteen pregnancies and raising eleven children. Also, her experience as a midwife in New York had convinced her that contraception was the only way to save poverty-stricken young mothers, whose 'weary misshapen bodies were destined to be thrown on the scrap heap before they were thirty-five'. Margaret Sanger founded the American Birth Control League, which led to the establishment of hundreds of family planning clinics all over America. Sanger announced the first clinic in 1916, but the opening was stopped by police. The first clinic to actually open was the Birth

Control Clinical Research Bureau in New York in 1923, but they were raided the following year, leading to the arrest of two women doctors and three nurses. The case was dismissed at trial, and by 1931 there were many clinics across America.

Change was slow, but in 1946 Sweden proposed a meeting of birth control organisations in Stockholm, and as a result the International Committee on Planned Parenthood was set up by the United States, Britain, the Netherlands and Sweden. In India in 1951 the first All-India Planning Conference was held, and in Bombay the following year the group met with the International Committee. From this meeting the International Planned Parenthood Federation was born, and there are now branches in countries all over the world.

Pioneers such as Marie Stopes and Margaret Sanger helped to change society's attitudes towards the use of contraception. Another of the great successes in the development of birth control, and one which had the biggest impact on women's lives, was the advent of the contraceptive pill. Women realised they would no longer have to struggle under the handicap of constantly bearing children. In the early 1960s a huge change took place in society due to the use of this new contraceptive. Without the fear of unwanted pregnancy restraining them, young women took full advantage of the new opportunities available. For the first time in history women were able to take full responsibility and control of their own bodies without consultation or co-operation from their partners, leading to greater sexual freedom and a surge of feminism.

It was not only women in the West who benefited from the introduction of the pill. Millions of women in underdeveloped countries were able to control their fertility for the first time, transforming their lives. Although other methods of birth control such as intrauterine devices (IUDs) and cervical caps had been available before the pill, most were highly unsuitable for women in poor nations, many of whom shared their home with a large family. Apart from the lack of basic necessities such as running water, there were many taboos regarding the touching of genitals. The lack of privacy needed to insert a cap and the lack of washing facilities to keep it clean prevented the use of barrier methods of this kind, and many male doctors would refuse to fit IUDs for women in their community.

The other obvious benefit of the pill was its reliability. The contraceptive pill offers 99 per cent protection against pregnancy, with failures mainly attributable to missed doses. In China, an ingenious idea ensures that a woman does not forget to take her contraceptive pill. Edible paper is impregnated with a contraceptive, and then printed in the form of a calendar. Each day a perforated square is torn off and eaten.

Another recent development in the field of contraception is the male birth control pill, which works by blocking the production of sperm. The pill is still being tested in clinical trials and has reached 90 per cent reliability; researchers have yet to find the most effective formulation, and at present the pills must be taken three times daily. A more appealing alternative to the male pill is an injectable male contraceptive. According to a recent announcement by Australian scientists, participants who received the injections every three to four months experienced no side effects and the injection was 100 per cent effective. The scientists also hope to produce a tablet version of the contraceptive within two to three years.

Research into new areas of contraception continues apace, such as the vas-occlusive methods, which block the flow of sperm by injection of a complex substance into the vas deferens. Alternatively a plug made of rubber or polyurethane can be inserted into the vas deferens. These methods are 98 per cent effective, fully reversible and have no effect on libido.

Despite such rapid technical achievements in the field of birth control, both men and women remain cautious, conscious of the effects of hormonal additives on the body. With the emergence of new methods of contraception it will be interesting to note in the future the number of men who will be prepared to take an active role in birth control. Traditional ideas and behaviour remain strong in fundamental areas of life such as conception and pregnancy. Changes in attitude can be very slow and take several generations to alter.

Men are perhaps slower to consider contraception as they do not have to deal with the physical consequences of unplanned pregnancies. As stated by the women's rights activist Florynce Kennedy, 'If men could get pregnant, abortion would be a sacrament.'

Conception

Societies through the ages have developed their own customs and rituals in an effort to promote childbearing and overcome any problems with infertility and many people around the world still place their faith in traditional superstitions.

In the West, despite major advances in the field of human-assisted fertility, medical science remains unable to help some people and couples still turn to traditional customs and rituals for aid.

The Cerne Abbas Giant in Dorset, carved from the chalk bedrock in the hillside, is thought to be a fertility god and is sometimes visited by couples hoping for a baby. The couples lie on the huge penis of the giant or, if feeling very bold, actually make love there in an attempt to harness some of the power from his vast bulk. Until quite recent times a maypole used to be set up near the giant.

The maypole dance derives from spring rituals glorifying the phallus and is still widely practised today. Some of the customs followed at Christmas time are also based on ancient fertility rites, such as the tradition of kissing under the mistletoe.

The Agony of Infertility

As the twentieth century progressed more practical methods of solving the problems associated with fertility developed. One such method – *in vitro* fertilisation – where an egg is fertilised outside the body, has become a well-known treatment for infertility over the last couple of decades. The work of Patrick Steptoe, Robert Edward and, later, Lord Robert Winston in this area has become legendary.

The pioneers of this treatment, Steptoe and Edward, realised early on in their research that obtaining funding for a prolonged research programme would be difficult as they faced strong opposition both from other members of the medical profession and some members of the general public. However, the determination of these and other scientists led to the successful birth of the first 'test tube baby' Louise Brown on 25 July 1978.

Serious ethical questions were provoked by their achievements, and many people were anxious, fearing that their success would be just the beginning of the manipulation of nature. Their groundbreaking research opened the door to future advances in the fields of genetic engineering and cloning. A particularly difficult issue arose because not all the embryos which were allowed to develop were reinserted in the womb of the mother. Many were opposed to experimentation on these embryos and the whole question of the moral status of the embryo itself arose.

Similarly, when women submit themselves for assisted conception they sometimes find themselves pregnant with multiple embryos and have to face the agonising decision of whether to agree to 'selective reduction'. Some, particularly those opposed to abortion, find they are unable to choose the life of one embryo over another, yet feel they have an obligation to save at least one life, even at the expense of another.

Just as hotly contested is the practice of surrogate motherhood, where a woman volunteers to carry a baby for a woman who is unable to bear it herself. Kim Cotton, Britain's first surrogate mother, campaigned for many years in an effort to persuade the Government that surrogate mothers should be paid for their labour, but all they are entitled to claim is expenses. The legal issues in cases where the surrogate mother decides to keep the baby are very complicated, particularly when the egg has been donated. It is not easy to decide who the 'natural mother' is, and to whom custody should be given.

The Legalisation of Terminations

According to Marie Stopes International, most unwanted pregnancies are the result of failed family planning methods; either accidents or improper use of contraceptives. Today, if a woman realises an accident has occurred, or if she has forgotten to take her pill, she is able to take hormone pills up to 72 hours after sex, or an IUD can be fitted up to five days afterwards. Both of these methods can prevent a pregnancy developing, but are not always successful.

In cases of unwanted pregnancy, many women turn to advisory organisations in order to investigate the options available to them. Despite a diverse range of freely available contraceptive methods, abortion remains a widespread method of birth control. In Britain in 2002 more than 173,000 abortions were carried out and in America forty million fetuses have been aborted since 1973. Legislation authorising the sale of the 'morning-after pill' over the counter was recently passed by Parliament in England in an effort to reduce these statistics.

The idea of selling drugs capable of inducing abortions over the counter is not new, and in Britain chemists sold such pills from the beginning of the twentieth century. One of these drugs, discovered by two French doctors, had an active abortifacient ingredient, known as apiol, which is extracted from parsley. Interestingly, parsley has been considered an effective method of birth control since the times of ancient Greece. Drug companies began to manufacture pills containing apiol in order to treat menstrual irregularity in the early years of the twentieth century, and these pills were widely used for ending unwanted pregnancies. Many of the drugs sold over the counter were ineffective for abortions, such as pennyroyal, Epsom salts and castor oil. Women would sometimes obtain abortifacients from chemists that were not sold for the purpose of ending a pregnancy. Lead pills, for example, were made by breaking pieces from lead plaster made to hold bandages together. These and other tablets containing arsenic and phosphorous were highly toxic and often fatal, not only for the fetus, but also for the mother. These 'medicines' were not withdrawn from sale until the 1950s.

Surgical methods of removing an unwanted fetus were also used by women, who were often so desperate they were willing to conduct the procedure themselves. Metal catheters continued to be used and became widely available, particularly in France. In the *Medical Record* of 1904 Frederick Griffith described how a pregnant woman would insert a catheter, dilate her cervix 'by rotary onward motion [...] until the sensation of rupture occurs and by the escape of bloody fluid proves the success of the operation'. That women were willing to suffer the emotional anguish and physical pain of performing their own abortions demonstrates the depth of desperation felt by many who surely would not have undertaken the procedure lightly.

Another method used by women in the early twentieth century was the syringe, which, when attached to a large rubber nozzle, would irrigate the walls of the uterus and flush out the fetus. Although highly effective, this method could be dangerous, introducing infection into the womb or air bubbles, which sometimes travelled to the heart or lungs.

From the late nineteenth century onwards more and more women approached doctors in an effort to persuade them to assist with ending their pregnancies. Reluctant to carry out dangerous procedures on their own bodies and wary of the pills and potions available in chemists, they wanted the medical profession to take responsibility. It was only once vacuum extraction (using suction to extract the fetus) became widely used by the medical profession that abortion could be carried out safely with minimum risks to health. This method was widely used in Russia during the 1920s but was not introduced in Britain until the late 1960s.

Although by the 1930s some doctors were taking responsibility for deciding whether or not to perform an abortion in hospital, many women still flocked to midwives or back-street abortionists. This situation continued until the 1960s, despite acknowledgement by many that women suffered both physically and emotionally as a result of enforced secrecy. *The Times* of 1965 reported the story of a young teenager who had been given quinine in order to procure an abortion. The dose had been too high and blindness resulted, but her pregnancy continued. Many tragic cases continued until 1967 when the Abortion Act was passed, allowing women to seek help from the medical profession.

Since then many debates have taken place not only as to whether it is morally right to legalise abortion, but also how late in pregnancy the procedure should be allowed to be carried out. In 1988 MP David Alton, in his private member's bill, failed to reduce the time limit on abortions from twenty-eight weeks to eighteen – the fifteenth unsuccessful attempt to alter the 1967 Abortion Act. It is increasingly difficult to define exactly when a fetus becomes viable, that is, capable of sustaining independent life, especially with the development of new techniques enabling doctors to sustain babies delivered at an earlier stage of gestation. With ever-improving medical treatment, doctors are able to save the lives of very tiny pre-term babies, some as young as twenty-two weeks gestation, so the age of viability continues to be reduced. As the law stands, abortion is allowed up to twenty-four weeks, or later if the mother's life is in danger.

According to Marie Stopes International, most abortions are carried out before the twelfth week of pregnancy, and this involves a fairly simple procedure of gentle suction. If a woman is less than nine weeks pregnant she can take the abortion pill, which causes miscarriage. Access to the abortion pill is restricted at the moment and is only available in hospital or private clinics but there are plans to widen the availability so that GPs and Family Planning Clinics can offer the treatment. Women have to obtain a certificate from two doctors before they can proceed with the procedure, which involves taking two different drugs over two days. The British Pregnancy Advisory Service has already allowed over a thousand women to take the abortion pill at home and it has been found to be safe and effective although sometimes very painful. Later abortions involve the use of instruments.

Today, despite new sophisticated medical techniques, there remain some complications for women following abortion, the most common being emotional trauma. Although many women are relieved once the stress and worry of their pregnancy has been removed, grief at the loss of their unborn child often strikes them at some stage in the future. Physical problems can also arise including uterine perforation, infections and complications with future pregnancies.

Abortion as a means of birth control has long been the subject of controversy. There are many groups who argue that a woman does not have the right to end life, referring to the sixth commandment 'Thou shalt not kill'. Others feel that life does not begin until later on in pregnancy, and defend a woman's right over her own body. Under continuing debate is the ultimate question of exactly when human life begins. Some people, such as those of Roman Catholic faith, believe that actual conception is the defining moment and consider the law to be too much in favour of women, ignoring the rights of the unborn child.

Achieving a balance between upholding a woman's right over her own body, yet not ignoring the rights of the unborn child has proved extremely difficult. Those in favour of abortion often view the embryo and fetus as a clump of cells and no more. They feel it is of utmost importance that women have control over their bodies and their future.

Some people argue that abortion can only be justified for specific reasons, such as if a woman's life or health is jeopardised by the pregnancy or birth, or if there is a strong likelihood that the child may be born with a severe mental or physical handicap. Many feel that pregnancy resulting from rape or incest also offers strong grounds for abortion. As the law stands the unborn fetus has no status and therefore no rights.

Expectant Mothers in the Second World War

During the Second World War it became much safer to have a baby in Britain, with maternal and infant mortality rates falling, despite bombs and the strain of war. Being an expectant mother brought with it a few luxuries that most of the population had to manage without, such as oranges, onions and real eggs. Vigilant neighbours could spot an expectant woman before the official announcement when she arrived home laden with bottles of concentrated orange juice (supplied by America) from the welfare clinic.

There was a sharp climb in the birth rate during the war years, partly perhaps as a result of the extra benefits available to pregnant women but mainly as the sense of insecurity created by the war stimulated an urge to confirm a marriage by procreation. The thought must have been in many women's minds that if their husband were killed, they would at least have his child. Women were beginning to be conscripted for war work, which also helped to increase the appeal of having a baby, and pregnancy was so common it was nicknamed 'the prevalent disease'.

Clothes rationing in 1941 meant women had to adapt existing clothes or live in one maternity dress for their entire pregnancy. Once the baby was born most mothers were sick of the sight of their maternity dress, and a ceremonial burning of their outfit became a popular tradition. Maternity wear was not even considered necessary before the twentieth century, as before this period women were generally expected to remain in seclusion once pregnant.

Plenty of advice was available from the Government on how to give a baby the best possible start in life, despite the difficulties that the war imposed. A good mixed diet was advocated, with plenty of green vegetables, orange juice, vitamins A and D, additional milk and eggs, plus an extra half-ration of meat per week. Through a special scheme, mothers and babies received supplies of blackcurrant juice and cod liver oil. During these years, pregnant women and children were better fed than ever before. Welfare foods were introduced in 1941, and the Ministry of Food produced the following advertisement, entitled 'Welcome Little Stranger':

'The very best welcome you can give your baby is a beautiful body, a contented disposition and a healthy, happy mother.'

Guessing the Sex

Often one of the most enjoyable aspects of pregnancy is the mystery and excitement involved in wondering whether the baby will be a boy or a girl, and most parents approach the birth with eager anticipation.

It is only very recently that parents have been able to discover the sex of their baby through the use of ultrasound scans. In previous centuries the sex of the unborn child was predicted using old wives' tales, such as heartburn and nausea signifying a girl, and lack of movement being a boy. A wedding ring was often suspended on a piece of cotton over the pregnant woman's abdomen; if it went in a circle the baby was a girl, but swinging to and fro meant a boy. It was believed that eating certain foods would secure the desired sex, such as bicarbonate of soda and sour things for a boy and sweet things to ensure a girl. This method of choosing the sex of a child by manipulating diet is receiving recognition today and apparently, if followed precisely, can be approximately 80 per cent accurate.

With the advancement of medical science some parents do not even need to speculate as to which sex their future baby will be. In America, parents are able to attend private clinics for selective fertility treatment in order to conceive a baby of a particular sex. Numerous couples in Britain are hoping for a change in the law so that they are able to balance their family, while others are so desperate for a child of a particular sex that they are prepared to travel abroad for the specialist treatment necessary.

EVE

Paving the Way to Safer Pregnancy

> We stand on the threshold of an age which is to herald the recognition of the mother and her child, to give public health work that human touch it has hitherto lacked, and to modify those glaring inequalities in social life and conditions which are destructive alike of infancy and the ideals of Christian citizenship.
> – From a speech by the Chairman of the Bradford Health Committee at the opening of the Municipal Maternity Home, 15 March, 1915

During the twentieth century a great number of advances, medical, social and scientific, combined to provide benefits to all members of society. Health and welfare issues became a priority. Events at the end of the nineteenth century increased the public's motivation to improve the circumstances in which they lived: the Boer War in 1899 demonstrated the poor health of the British nation, with 40 per cent of volunteers being deemed medically unfit to serve.

As the new century approached, vital scientific breakthroughs led to safer medical treatment. Once doctors implemented stringent levels of hygiene the number of patients dying as a result of infection declined significantly. By the 1890s dressings were exposed to steam, instruments were boiled and rubber gloves were introduced. These and other advances paved the way for safe and effective Caesarean births.

Despite the undeniable improvements, however, maternal and perinatal mortality remained high at the beginning of the twentieth century. Obstetric care was still in its infancy, with many problems still to be solved. Over the following 100 years many major medical and scientific advances had a huge impact on the care of the childbearing woman. With the perfection of the Caesarean and development of more effective analgesics, childbirth towards the middle of the century became a much safer experience for women. However, one of the most important developments in the effort to reduce maternal mortality was the growing attention to antenatal care.

MRS. BALDWIN'S MESSAGE.

Every thinking man and woman deplores unnecessary suffering. We have our societies for the protection of children and animals, but the unnecessary suffering of mothers in childbirth is apt to be ignored. We ask you to help to make this a thing of the past, both by propaganda and by supporting the work of this fund.

Lucy Baldwin

VISCOUNTESS SNOWDEN'S MESSAGE.

Is there a man who would not have sacrificed everything to have saved his Mother unnecessary suffering at his birth? With that in his heart, he simply cannot say "No" to this appeal for the Mothers of our country.

Ethel Snowden

DAME MARGARET LLOYD GEORGE'S MESSAGE.

Not only of Motherhood do I ask you to think. I would that you remember your own Mother, her love, her ceaseless care and concern.

With that lovely memory prompting you, how can you fail to make your gift that Motherhood may be as safe as it is noble?

Margaret Lloyd George

YOUR DONATION

There are 44,000,000 people in Great Britain, and 44,000,000 shillings when invested, would enable the National Birthday Trust Fund to attain its object.

We ask for Birthday Donations to help the Birthdays of others, either 1/-, or the number of shillings (or pounds) according to the number of birthdays you have celebrated.

Please send 1/- now, and 1/- on each birthday, if you cannot send more.

Signatures of leading supporters of a 'Safer Motherhood' campaign from the early years of the twentieth century

The Growth of Antenatal Care

Mothers in America were the first to receive special care while pregnant. In 1901 nurses in Boston began visiting pregnant women in their district to advise on matters of health and hygiene during pregnancy, and by 1909 they were visiting patients every ten days during pregnancy offering support and guidance. The medical profession began to realise that the health of the fetus was directly affected by the health of the mother. It was also discovered that dangerous complications of pregnancy such as pre-eclampsia could be detected early enough to be treated if pregnant women were monitored regularly.

SAFER MOTHERHOOD,

Extension of
Maternity Services
(including Anæsthetics).

National Birthday Trust Fund,
Empire House,
175, Piccadilly,
London, W.1.

'Safer Motherhood' sticker promoting extended maternity services

In Britain progress was slower. Although health visiting had begun in the 1860s, it did not extend to expectant mothers. John Ballantyne, a Scottish gynaecologist, began to consider how the health of infants could be improved, and he decided to pilot a study in 1901 that monitored pregnant women and reported any abnormalities. By 1915 the first antenatal clinic had opened in the United Kingdom. Although good news for women, midwives were sceptical and concerned that they would lose their patients to hospitals if they attended clinics for regular antenatal checks. This led some midwives to discourage patients from attending the clinics. Not until 1936 was the midwife's position secured by the introduction of salaried positions under local authorities.

Long waiting times and fear of the dreaded 'internal' deterred some women from registering for antenatal care. Others, particularly those from the middle classes, felt that the clinics were involved in some way with illegitimate births and avoided them. Being pregnant out of wedlock brought shame to families and stigmatised the children born under such circumstances.

For those women who did attend, medical care in the antenatal clinics varied from place to place. In most areas women were advised on matters of nutrition and other ways of maintaining their health, but few tests were conducted until the 1960s. The ability to monitor the progress of the unborn child was limited; doctors and midwives could determine the size of the fetus and its position in the womb, but they could only guess whether it was healthy and had no idea of its sex until birth.

In the 1960s a breakthrough in antenatal care was made when it was discovered that some cells from the fetus could be extracted by amniocentesis (withdrawing a sample of amniotic fluid to check for abnormalities) and examined to ascertain genetic information, such as the existence of spina bifida. Once ultrasound scanning was introduced other defects could be identified and amniocentesis became safer by allowing the position of the placenta to be pinpointed. Until then doctors used the 'pray and plunge' method.

Once established, antenatal care contributed to the 'clinicalisation' of a natural process. Women's groups were keen for the Government to address the social and economic situations in which mothers had to raise their babies, in order to lower the number of maternal and infant deaths, but consultant obstetricians advised that to overcome the poor statistics the birth process should be dealt with more scientifically. When mortality rates were examined from the Netherlands, Denmark and Sweden it was reported that Britain compared poorly despite, or perhaps because of, the greater involvement of doctors in the birthing process. Care of the pregnant mother in these countries was still largely in the hands of midwives. Housing and diet were eventually acknowledged to play a part in the future health of both mother and child and efforts were made to improve social conditions.

Technological advances have created a wide spectrum of prenatal tests that provide doctors with a great deal of previously unavailable information. Difficult decisions have to be made by today's parents as to whether to consent to testing when pregnant. All women in Britain are now offered a test to ascertain the likelihood that the baby they are carrying could have Down syndrome. If the test result shows a high possibility then they must decide whether to have an amniocentesis. This test carries approximately 1 per cent chance of miscarriage, in which case a woman may lose a perfectly healthy baby in an attempt to ascertain its health. Unfortunately, human fallibility can never be eliminated. There have been cases of women being advised that the baby they are carrying is affected by Down syndrome in error. Also the stress of numerous tests and the harrowing wait for results may have a detrimental effect on the health of the mother.

Despite the drawbacks, the sophistication of antenatal care now available undoubtedly saves lives, both of mothers and babies. Any woman who has been recognised as suffering from pre-eclampsia by observant midwives will no doubt attest to the benefits of modern day healthcare.

Problems and Intervention

During the twentieth century major developments in various areas of medical research had enormous importance for the field of obstetrics. Penicillin, one of the greatest discoveries of the twentieth century, paved the way for safe childbirth for women. After war broke out in 1939 there was a great need for antibiotics to treat the terrible war wounds, but Britain was so stretched by the war effort that penicillin research and production was limited. It was only when America offered assistance to Britain that penicillin began to be used extensively, proving to be highly effective against puerperal fever.

Further studies into infection revealed that many cases of puerperal fever had resulted from the transference of bacteria from the nose or throat of the doctors attending labouring women.

By the 1920s attention to the welfare of mothers had become unavoidable. Despite the dangers of diseases such as tuberculosis, death in childbirth claimed 17 per cent of all women's lives; of all the hazardous occupations in the country, including mining and seafaring, motherhood was the most dangerous. Over 3,000 women every year died in England and Wales and thousands more were damaged or invalided as a result of childbirth. Politicians were keen to stop the falling birth rate, but persuading women to have more children when the dangers were so apparent was no easy task.

It was clear that welfare services needed to be improved, thereby reducing the maternal mortality rates. Various areas in need of improvement were highlighted by Dr Janet Campbell, Senior Medical Officer to the Ministry of Health, in her Government report on maternal mortality in 1924. The main areas for concern in her opinion were sanitation and housing, rickets (and the resulting difficult deliveries), abortion and miscarriage (leading to sepsis), the employment of women and the quality of obstetric medical care. Pressure on the Government increased, particularly following a Government report in 1932 which revealed that 45.9 per cent of maternal deaths had been due to a 'primary avoidable factor'.

New antiseptic routines were introduced into hospitals and improved hygiene served to reduce maternal mortality rates.

Another great danger to the life of a labouring woman had always been the possibility of haemorrhage. Rapid blood loss almost always led to surgical shock and then death. The use of the drug ergometrine helped in the treatment of haemorrhage by causing blood vessels to contract, but the blood lost could not safely be replaced until blood transfusion became possible.

Surgeons found that they were unable to safely replace blood due to a strange reaction in the body when the blood was donated. By 1901 the Viennese doctor and medical researcher Karl Landsteiner discovered agglutins in the blood and classified human blood into four groups. By 1915 surgeons were able to give patients the correct blood group, and by 1930 blood banks were set up. Once war broke out in 1939 a national blood donation scheme was organised.

Increased medical and obstetric knowledge and treatment meant that childbirth became more managed than ever before, and a new era of medical intervention in the birth process began. Intervention was seen as a way of avoiding damage resulting from a complicated delivery and was strongly recommended by obstetrician Joseph B. DeLee of Chicago. He recommended the use of episiotomy and forceps for all births, even routine cases, and the administration of a drug to hasten the delivery of the placenta, which would then be removed using a 'shoehorn manoeuvre'. DeLee felt that if all births were attended in this way damage to the mother and baby during birth would be greatly reduced. His suggestions became very popular in America and were widely followed in the 1930s.

By the 1940s episiotomies had become common practice in most Western hospitals, although the procedure was largely carried out without local anaesthetic until the 1970s. This treatment never gained widespread popularity in Britain except in cases of necessity. However, as more and more women entered hospital for childbirth, medical intervention increased and strict aseptic techniques were followed. These included careful preparation of the woman for labour: shaving the vulva and administering an enema.

Doctors also dictated the optimum position for delivery, but unfortunately it was the position that most suited them rather than their patients. Throughout the nineteenth century British women were generally advised to lie on their left side for delivery, as it was felt in Victorian society that this position was the most modest. By the 1920s obstetricians were advising that women should lie on their backs with their feet in stirrups. Lying back during birth is now thought to affect blood pressure adversely, decrease intensity of contractions and increase the need for forceps and episiotomy. In the Netherlands the sitting position is always used, and use of a vacuum extractor or forceps in childbirth rarely exceeds 4 per cent compared with some American hospitals where the incidence can rise to as high as 65 per cent.

Another intervention used by obstetricians was the early induction of labour as it was felt to be beneficial to the mother to give birth before the baby got too large. Little consideration was given to the welfare of the baby and possible damage caused as a result of prematurity. It was actually considered beneficial to 'shake the apple off the tree' a couple of weeks before term by administering castor oil or quinine orally in an attempt to stimulate the uterus into action; usually the only effect produced was nausea.

In the 1950s the focus shifted from the mother to the baby, as doctors were more able to check the wellbeing of the fetus in the womb. Intervention was seen as necessary if labours were prolonged in order to benefit the child. Once sophisticated methods to monitor fetal heartbeat during labour became available in the 1960s, intervention further increased. Averages were taken for the length of time women spent in labour and from this a 'normal' duration was calculated. If labour did not follow the average, a drip was set up to speed up or slow down contractions. Pain relief in these instances was often essential and in many cases pethidine was used. The action of this analgesic slowed down contractions and the stimulant oxytocin was given to speed them up. A vicious circle such as this and the resulting high use of drugs was later connected with the high incidence of fetal distress. A large number of births were induced not only in the apparent interest of safety for mother and baby, but also for the convenience of the hospital and the incidence rose steadily from 27 per cent of all births in England and Wales in 1970 to 40 per cent in the mid-seventies.

Improving Pain Relief
With childbirth becoming safer the next problem to combat was pain during labour. Until the late nineteenth century, not much existed in the way of pain relief for a woman during birth, apart from a board at the foot of the bed to brace herself on and a piece of rubber to bite on. Sincere thanks were given to God if a woman survived the 'great pain and peril of childbirth'.

Since gaining the approval of Queen Victoria, chloroform was widely used as a pain reliever during labour, but towards the end of the nineteenth century its dangerous side effects were realised. It was difficult to administer the correct dosage, and there was a growing number of deaths from its use in surgery, leading to demands for a safer alternative. As the new century approached a cocktail of scopolamine and morphine was developed in Germany which became known as Twilight Sleep. It was so named because once administered by injection it would send the patient to sleep and when they awoke they would enter a 'twilight' state. Its use over the next forty years became almost universal, but it was not without its problems: the required dose was different for every woman, and in many women a considerable amount of time elapsed between the administration of the first dose and the patient's passing into 'twilight sleep'.

Twilight Sleep eventually fell into disuse as other, more satisfactory drugs became available. One such drug, which is still widely used, is pethidine, which was introduced in Germany in 1939. Although a strong analgesic, pethidine is not without side effects and, like most chemical substances, can be diffused from the mother's bloodstream to the baby's via the membrane of the placenta, the organ which supplies the fetus with its life-supporting requirements. If this occurs the baby's respiration can be depressed and an antidote is sometimes necessary if the baby is badly affected.

Another analgesic that remains popular today is Entonox, a combination of nitrous oxide and oxygen, which is inhaled. The benefit of this combination is that it has few side effects. Its use superseded Trilene, an inhalational analgesic available in Britain in the 1950s.

It was the development of epidural analgesia that finally revolutionised the control of pain during labour. It was in use by the First World War in general medicine, but was later adapted for use in obstetrics. It involves injecting a local anaesthetic solution into the lumbar region of the spine, which then induces a condition of temporary paraplegia. One of the greatest benefits of the epidural is that women are now able to remain conscious during Caesarean sections if they choose to and can participate fully in the excitement of the birth and hold the baby straight after delivery.

Despite the benefits of epidural analgesia it is still a far from perfect method. Although extremely effective in relieving all pain, there are considerable drawbacks for some women. Many women are unable to feel the urge to push during the final stage of labour, and so the incidence of forceps is much higher. In some cases its use has even been known to cause death.

The Move from Home to Hospital

Throughout the twentieth century hospitals improved their surroundings and analgesia became widely available. The National Health Service was established in the United Kingdom in 1948, and consequently the trend towards hospital births began to spiral upwards. Until the twentieth century the majority of women stayed at home to deliver their baby, attended by a midwife and close female relatives. As the early years of the new century passed more people became involved in overseeing the birth process and by the 1930s pregnant and labouring women could be cared for by a number of healthcare professionals including hospital consultants, GPs, midwives and local authority staff in antenatal clinics.

Despite increased involvement by the medical profession, morbidity rates remained high, and as a result the Committee on Maternal Mortality and Morbidity was set up by the Ministry of Health in 1929. It concluded that the high death rates were due to complications of pregnancy and increased supervision and clinicalisation of the birth process were thought to be solutions to the problem. Health professionals therefore became convinced that pregnancy should be treated as an illness and labour 'management' increased.

As a result of increased concern for the health of women, the British College of Obstetricians and Gynaecologists was also formed in 1929, which eventually led to a move from home to hospital for most labouring women. The Ministry of Health and health professionals felt that the main causes of death, sepsis and haemorrhage, could be managed far more effectively by doctors in a hospital environment.

Ironically it was still sometimes doctors themselves who increased a woman's risk of puerperal fever. They interfered in the process of birth far more frequently than midwives, increasing the potential for bacteria to enter the bloodstream, and they were often careless with personal hygiene and sterilisation routines. Despite the drawbacks, women were gradually lured towards the hospital environment by the availability of increasingly effective analgesia provided there; midwives were not allowed to administer pain-relieving drugs at home. Additionally, improved surgical techniques, prevention of eclampsia and successful blood transfusions provided women with greater advantages than ever before, even if their chances of undergoing a Caesarean or forceps delivery was far greater than that of home births.

Poorer women were slower to attend hospital to deliver though; they found it difficult to find carers to look after their children at home, and they had to manage as best they could caring for their family themselves from the moment their baby was born if they could not find help from relatives or neighbours. Unhygienic surroundings often faced those who went to attend women in poor families, as demonstrated in a letter to the *British Medical Journal* in 1921:

> You find a bed which has been slept on by the husband, wife and one or two children; it has frequently been soaked with urine, the sheets are dirty, and the patient's garments soiled; she has not had a bath. Instead of sterile dressings you have a few old rags, or the discharges are allowed to soak into the nightdress which is not changed for days.

It was known that poor hygiene contributed to the deaths of mothers and babies, yet the items needed to reduce the risk were unattainable by average families. The *Motherhood Book* of 1934 listed the necessary items for a home delivery, but in reality women were forced to replace items such as rubber sheets with brown paper, and newspaper was often used instead of swabs.

In *Lark Rise to Candleford*, Flora Thompson described labour equipment that was shared around the community when the need arose:

> The box appeared simultaneously with every new baby [...] It contained half a dozen of everything – tiny shirts, swathes, long flannel barrows, nighties, and napkins made, and kept in repair, and lent for every confinement by the clergyman's daughter.

In the 1930s the Women's Co-operative Guild and Women's Labour League encouraged the Government to make more 'maternity bags' available to working-class women. These bags contained some essentials for use during labour, but unfortunately, such was the shame associated with accepting charity, that many women declined to accept the offer.

With the implementation of plans for a National Health Service in 1948, many more women opted for care in a hospital environment. They were assured of care throughout their pregnancy and birth, without the necessity of means testing: free health facilities were promised for everyone. By 1974, 95.6 per cent of births took place in a hospital environment, and in 1996, despite the turning tide towards more natural births, only 2 per cent of mothers in the UK chose to give birth at home.

In America the move towards hospitals took place earlier than in Britain. Hospitals in the USA advertised themselves as being germ-free environments and going to hospital appealed to many women as it meant avoiding the messiness of birth 'polluting' their homes. In 1920s America the cost of hospital treatment was high, with no health insurance plans in existence, but couples were encouraged to save up for the very best care they could provide for their future infant. The hospital environment was pleasant and homely, and by the 1930s nearly three-quarters of all American births took place in hospital.

Unfortunately most American women did not receive value for money. Despite the large increase in the number of hospital births between 1915 and 1930, there was no decline in the number of maternal deaths, and the number of infant deaths actually increased. Most mothers admitted into an American hospital received the standard treatment; they were wheeled into a delivery room, rolled onto their backs, and had their feet placed in stirrups. If uncooperative, they had their arms and legs strapped down. Painkillers were given as a matter of course and this often necessitated the administration of drugs to speed up contractions. Forceps would often be used, and to facilitate an easier birth for the attendants an episiotomy would be carried out. Following investigations it was found that doctors and other attendants frequently intervened unnecessarily without paying sufficient attention to hygiene.

In an effort to curb the disturbing statistics staff were strictly supervised and those in authority ensured that from around 1930 onwards aseptic techniques were practised. The new routines brought dividends to mothers and mortality rates fell dramatically.

The widespread use of intervention and pain relief during labour in Britain has ensured that control of the birth process remains in the hands of doctors and most births take place in a hospital environment.

The Natural Birth Movement

Following the improvement of the Caesarean section and a number of other obstetric intervention techniques, women in the latter part of the twentieth century were able to enter pregnancy with more than a reasonable expectation that they would have a healthy baby following labour, and that they would be fit and able to care for the baby themselves. Weakening taboos regarding women's bodies and improved sexual knowledge helped to relieve some of the anxiety associated with childbirth. Until this time some mothers, in their innocence, had no idea from where their baby would be born, right up to the moment of birth. One woman remembered her first labour with anguish in the gynaecologist Grantly Dick-Read's *Childbirth Without Fear* of 1942:

> I remember at the very last minute I suddenly realised where it was coming from. It shook me. I was so shocked. No, I didn't know before. I don't know what I thought. But suddenly knowing that this child would have to come out of there. I knew the size of a … Oh, I was so shocked and frightened. I said, 'Please, please, can you stop it coming out? I don't mind what pain I have. I'll suffer any pain but please can you stop it coming out?'

For the first time in history childbirth did not necessarily mean excruciating pain and possible infection and death. Despite this, many women began to feel that something was missing from their labour and that the level of medical intervention had turned a uniquely special moment in life into an aseptic and sterile experience.

One of the first pioneers towards a safe but also enjoyable birth was Grantly Dick-Read. He began to examine the conveyor belt system of care offered in hospitals in the 1940s following a visit to a labouring woman in London. She refused his offer of chloroform during the birth of her baby as she felt no pain. She had told him, 'It didn't hurt. It wasn't meant to, was it doctor?'

This one incident led him to believe that women in labour feel pain as a result of fear and tension in the body, rather than from childbirth itself. He felt that if women were educated on the process of birth and not told to expect intense pain, they would be much less likely to require any pain relief. The National Childbirth Trust was formed in 1956 in an effort to promote these ideas and bring them to the attention of a wider audience.

From this time women began to question the circumstances in which they had given birth and many regretted that the experience had been so hazy through the use of drugs. Some only remembered the struggle of trying to form a bond with a baby who was offered to them once it had been washed, powdered and dressed. A new quest to gain control over the birth experience had begun.

A change in America came following publication of a book entitled *Painless Childbirth* by Ferdinand Lamaze, a French obstetrician. He had studied ancient folk practices that were used in Russia in the 1940s. Psychoprophylaxis, a method by which a patient concentrated the mind on extraneous sensations, had apparently been used successfully to counteract pain. He added a rapid shallow breathing system to the principles already established and the practice became known as the 'Lamaze method'. The method became popular in America following publication of another book, *Thank you, Dr Lamaze*, written by an American woman living in France. She had been so grateful for the new techniques during her birth experience that she was moved to write about it. Not only did the technique empower women during birth, but it also gave them a sense of confidence, as they felt that the principles were based in science. For the first time since the take-over by doctors, women were beginning to view themselves as active participants in the birth process.

During the 1960s other birth philosophies began to emerge in the new climate of change. Dr Frederic Leboyer in France shifted the attention from the mother to the child. He felt that birth must be a terrible experience for a baby and the proof of this was the tortured faces and desperate screams of all infants when born. Leboyer wanted to create a soft, gentle atmosphere in which babies could be born, and he suggested that newborns should immediately be placed on their mother's stomach to be softly massaged. These principles were followed to some extent in earlier centuries when it was felt that newborns should be kept in an environment that simulated their life in the womb.

Leboyer was not the first to write in this regard. Around 1930, Maria Montessori, the first Italian woman doctor, wrote about the shock of exposing a newborn to a harsh new environment:

> He arrives in the adult world with delicate eyes which have never seen daylight and ears which have never known noise. His body, hitherto unbruised, is now exposed to rough contact with the soulless hands of an adult who disregards that delicacy which should be respected.

Michel Odent, a French obstetrician, took Leboyer's ideas a step further and set up a special unit at his hospital in France, his main aim being the demedicalisation of the birth process. He encouraged women to take whichever position felt most natural to them, whether it be standing or squatting and, in an effort to promote relaxation, he introduced birthing pools. He rarely used forceps or analgesia and found that Caesareans were almost entirely unnecessary, particularly in cases such as breech births. It was now becoming possible for women to give birth in hospital with all technology available if necessary, but to recreate the more relaxing environment of home.

From the late sixties, both in Britain and America, feminists were pushing for women to accept responsibility for the birth process and regain control from male doctors. The publication of a book entitled *Birth at Home* by Sheila Kitzinger in 1979 added to calls for home birth to be an available choice for women, rather than an exception. Although in Britain only about 1 to 2 per cent of births take place at home, in the Netherlands homebirths account for around half of the total number of births in the country. Their maternal and infant mortality statistics suggest that birth in the home is no more dangerous than in hospital.

Although for some forty years now movements such as the National Childbirth Trust have been campaigning for new approaches to childbirth, where mothers have a right to choose to have their baby free from interference, doctors and sometimes midwives persist in using technology which clinicalises the birth process, even when mothers are resistant to this.

When a woman experiences difficulties during birth, either physically or through bad relations with medical staff, it can turn the event of childbirth into a negative experience, sometimes even adversely affecting the relationship between mother and baby. Modern mothers should be hugely grateful for the phenomenal scientific successes of the last century that have enabled doctors to help those who would otherwise have died in childbirth, but birthing movements and feminist groups insist they should also have the right to 'birth without violence' when there is no danger of damage to mother or baby.

Midwives

Despite the increased involvement of hospital doctors and GPs attending childbearing women, midwives still played a dominant role in their care in Britain. By 1902 a Midwives' Bill was passed by Parliament that confirmed registration and licensing matters, and reasserted that midwives should be supervised to ensure efficient practices. The passing of this bill guaranteed the future for midwives, although GPs were initially concerned that the income they received from attending births would be threatened. Once the National Insurance Act of 1911 was passed, however, GPs saw their income would be sufficient without maternity fees, promoting greater harmony between the professions.

Formal training for midwives in the early 1920s was limited to a three-month course, recommended by the Central Midwives Board. Gradually the duration of training increased, particularly as financial support for women in training began to develop, and by 1937 a two-year training course was provided for midwives. At this time local authorities assumed responsibility for paying them a salary. It also became the responsibility of the local authority to provide doctors with extra payments whenever they dealt with a labouring woman. Some felt that this led to a large number of women being subjected to 'managed' births that would otherwise have been straightforward.

While midwives were reassured that their long-term position was secure, they were disappointed that the British College of Obstetricians would not allow them to administer pain relief in the home. They were permitted to administer gas and air but as the equipment necessary was both expensive and cumbersome most were unable to provide it for their patients. The British Medical Association had also recommended that it was the GP's decision as to whether a midwife could care for a woman, and, as a result, midwives ended up dealing with only straightforward 'normal' births.

In America the midwives' battle for survival was considerably less successful than their British counterparts. With the increased activity of doctors, the role and status of midwives declined rapidly, a trend encouraged by the medical profession. Doctors with a vested interest in taking over the midwife's role in providing support for a labouring woman promoted a picture of midwives as dirty, superstitious and medically ignorant, however, despite their propaganda, the working classes in particular still relied on the services provided by midwives.

As the years passed American midwives were doomed to disappear. No formal training was offered to them and midwifery was made illegal in 1935. Care of the pregnant woman then took place in hospital by specially trained maternity nurses.

The Rise of Doctors

While the medical profession was keen to take over from midwives in an effort to lower the mortality rates, there was little or no special training provided for doctors. Until the twentieth century knowledge of the birth process had been passed from generation to generation by women and midwives who learned their craft from one another. Suddenly medical students were thrown into real-life situations and were expected to deal with patients in labour with thoroughly inadequate training and no practical experience.

The difficulty for the doctors was that the BMA had insisted they decide which cases the midwife should be allowed to deal with, and consequently the doctors were left with complicated births, never having enough 'normal' cases to practise and gain experience from. Mothers who were allocated GPs to attend to them during labour were no doubt unaware that they were actually at the poor end of the bargain. As a result of inexperience and overwork doctors tended to deal with childbirth in a hurry, often using newly manufactured drugs which sped up the action of the uterus, in order to be able to deal with many other calls waiting.

Forceps were also often used unnecessarily in an attempt to speed up delivery, and sometimes their use ended in disaster. Douglas Miller noted in the *British Medical Journal* of 1928 that one in ten mothers died as a result of the use of forceps and two-thirds of those babies delivered by forceps also died. Interestingly, during the First World War there had been an unexpected drop in the number of maternal mortalities and it was later acknowledged that it had probably occurred as a result of the large number of doctors called away for war duties. Female midwives provided almost all maternity care during these years.

While doctors today are still involved in the care of childbearing women, the introduction of 'domino' schemes have served to increase contact with midwives both during pregnancy and birth. The scheme allows community midwives to bring their own patients into hospital so that they can continue their care and deliver the baby themselves. They then accompany the mother home following a short rest in hospital after the birth.

The Natural Birth Movement, formed in the 1950s, has worked for many years to encourage women to regain control of the birth process, and organisations such as the National Childbirth Trust continue the campaign.

Traditions from around the World
Until comparatively recently in Britain women in labour were surrounded by female friends and relatives, and men were forbidden from entering the woman's domain. In a relatively short period of time, protocol in the birthing chamber has completely altered. It is

now unusual for fathers to wait outside for news of the birth of their child, except perhaps for those of a squeamish nature.

In some traditional societies around the world it is also thought to be advantageous for the father to be present during the birth. Among the Kalmyk Mongolians, for example, the father and other male relatives attend the labour up until the moment the baby is ready to be born. Many women find the presence of their male partner comforting and supportive, and enjoy sharing the birth experience with them. However, there are still some women who feel that their husband would not see them in the same light if they were with them during the birth, and they prefer a close female relative or friend to accompany them.

Men in ancient China tried to strengthen their sperm by having intercourse with as many women as possible without ejaculating. They imagined that their partner was grossly ugly or gnashed their teeth a thousand times in an attempt to prevent ejaculation.

In America, 'doulas' are becoming popular as birth attendants. The word refers to the most important female servant in the ancient Greek household. A doula supports a woman throughout her childbearing experience and facilitates communication between the labouring woman and other birth attendants. Many women find it helpful to have somebody who can promote smooth communication between them and the medical staff. The main objective of a doula is to nurture and protect the woman's memory of the birth of her baby, which is seen as a key life experience.

All over the world today there are still a great number of superstitions that govern the way in which a woman gives birth. Madagascan women usually settle themselves in a room partitioned off from the rest of the house when their labour begins, accompanied by older women who help with the delivery. They believe that heat is very helpful during labour, and traditionally friends would arrive at the house with money for firewood. A fire is lit in the room even during the warmest times of the year.

A complex sequence of rituals are followed by Hindu families in northern India in order to ensure the safety of the mother and child from birth onwards. Each ritual is intended to transfer any ill omens from angry ancestor gods away from the labour room in order to give the baby the best possible chance for survival. The birth attendants circle rupees over the mother to speed up delivery and remove danger from spirits. These coins are later given to the priest's wife. Once the baby is born a female relative washes the mother's breasts to purify them. She then fills a saucer with milk, puts a coin in it and uses blades of grass to sprinkle the milk over the mother's breasts. Again this coin is removed following the ritual to remove the dangerous influences from ancestor gods.

> If a wife, proud of the greatness of her relatives or her own excellence, violates the duty which she owes to her lord [husband] the king shall cause her to be devoured by dogs.
> – from *The Laws of Manu*, a Hindu religious text, c. 500 BC

Mother and child are protected by appeasing the gods. On the sixth day after birth the midwife returns to the labour room and performs a ceremony to the goddess Bemata as it is thought that she placed the baby in the womb. Five pieces of fried bread are set out, one for each leg of the cot and one for the goddess. A lamp filled with mustard oil is placed at the head end of the cot. Two trays are filled, one with grain and another with sugar and flour. An image of the goddess is made from cow dung and is covered with a cloth. The mother squats down next to the cot holding her newborn baby and some grain is passed to her, which she then offers to Bemata. Everything is then taken out of the room in order to remove any bad omens.

Following birth, Hindu mothers are considered to be in an impure state, and this can be remedied by a bath, as running water is considered to be a great purification agent. The new mother is then reintegrated into society. Her infant is also elaborately bathed, then massaged with oil and tightly wrapped in a sari.

All Hindu women in India are normally confined following childbirth, but the duration of impurity of each woman depends on her caste. Members of the Brahman priestly caste are only impure for up to ten days, but lower castes are impure for up to forty days. Following confinement a woman visits the temple with the baby to be blessed, and the baby is given a name.

In other societies ancestors are believed to be helpful to the birth process and their influence is not feared but welcomed. According to an Australian Aboriginal myth a woman must be entered by a spirit in order to give birth to a live baby, and pregnant mothers will therefore ensure that they walk through special places where totemic ancestors have left spirit entities. Despite the undeniable involvement of women in the birth process, Aboriginal men claim the glory, as they are believed to possess the power to cause birth.

In some Jewish communities a woman in her ninth month of pregnancy and her husband are permitted to open the ark during Shabbat services. They pray that the woman's womb will open with ease during the birth, just as the ark opens with ease to allow them to remove the Torah (the book of the law) from inside.

For many tribes around the world the anxiety and problems that arise during childbirth are countered by a comforting sequence of rituals. Maasai women usually give birth at home, and the midwife follows traditional custom as she cuts the cord by saying 'you are now responsible for your life, as I am responsible for mine'. She then proceeds to wash both mother and baby with a mixture of water and milk. The father is informed of the birth by the midwife, and if the child is a girl he has to go and draw blood from the jugular vein of a heifer and make a mock attempt to do the same from a bullock. If the child is a boy then the opposite must be done. The blood from the appropriate animal is then mixed with milk which the mother must drink. A ram is then slaughtered and eaten by the mother and birth attendants, and this feast is followed by prayers. The following day a sheep is slaughtered, the best meat is given to the midwife and the fat is melted down to make another drink for the mother.

> Australian Aborigines attempted a form of sterilisation by making an incision under the penis so that the semen would leak out through the hole rather than entering the woman. Usually the laziest, weakest or most unpopular members of the tribe were operated on in this way.

The Hua people of the highlands of Papua New Guinea believe that a woman can pollute a man with either her menstrual blood or fluids from childbirth. They believe that when a woman loses this fluid her body becomes 'cleaner' but that this fluid may then contaminate someone else. Childbirth cleanses her, and so if she has many children by old age she may have rid her body of all pollution. When she is first married, however, she is viewed as extremely unclean, and male members of the community will not even eat food prepared by her until her first child is born. The first child is considered to take much pollution away from the mother and is therefore regarded as extremely unclean. As a consequence of this belief some Hua fathers are afraid to touch their firstborn but may poke it playfully with a stick.

In many cultures around the world today it is still thought necessary to confine a mother for a certain length of time following birth for ritual cleansing. A new mother in Palau, Micronesia, is isolated for four days after she has given birth, and is ritually bathed eight times each day by her midwife, then anointed with coconut oil mixed with turmeric and rubbed with rebotel leaves, a plant native to the island.

Following birth it is traditional in many societies for mothers to have a quiet period of confinement in order to recover from the ordeal of childbirth, but some cultures follow a custom of couvade, in which both father and mother withdraw from the outside world for a certain length of time. In the countries where couvade is still practised, both parents need to be reintroduced into society. The Buka people of the Solomon Islands expect to see new parents in the village on the fourth day after birth, but the father is not allowed to hunt or fish, and neither parent is permitted to eat meat or fish for some time afterwards.

Among the Paiutes of Northern Nevada it was customary for the father to assume all household tasks for twenty-five days after his partner had given birth. If he did not also do his fair share of caring for the child he would be considered an outcast. Once the baby was born a family was given five baskets in which to lay the newborn, and every five days the basket was changed for a new one. At the end of twenty-five days the umbilical cord was put into the last basket and all five baskets would be tied to a tree. This was believed to make the bonds of the family strong.

In Britain the tradition of churching women following childbirth survived unofficially until well into the twentieth century, then slowly fell into decline. The *American Prayer Book* of 1979 still featured a modified version of the churching ceremony. The Church of England taught that childbirth was not an unclean act and therefore being churched did not involve purification, only the offering of thanks to the Lord for his generous gift and for the wellbeing of the mother. My own grandmother went straight to church on her first day out of bed following the birth of my mother to 'thank the Lord I got through it' as she put it.

Newborns in some communities are protected in their early, most vulnerable days by a variety of customs. In Romania it is traditional to bathe a new baby in hot water and mark its forehead with white ash, while in West Africa some parents still practise an age-old ritual of passing a young baby over the coffin of an aged relative to deter the dead person's spirit from interfering with the child.

In northern Spain a number of newborn babies are arranged in a line on a mattress in a special ceremony that relates to the massacre of the innocents story from the Bible. A man leaps over the babies, symbolising the danger they face, and when he lands on the ground their escape from this danger is represented.

It remained popular in Britain for much of the twentieth century to ensure that when a baby was born it went up before going down. It was thought that if a baby were to succeed in life they must go up, and people would often take newborns to the top of the house, or climb a chair or ladder with the baby in their arms. The tradition of bringing a new baby a gift is widely practised to the present day and in some cultures the gift is specified by local custom. In the Outer Hebrides the crossing of the baby's hand with silver was thought to ensure future prosperity.

Some mothers still practised the protective tradition of dressing babies in clothes of the opposite sex through the early part of the twentieth century in an attempt to deceive the Devil. This is not the only reason, however. In Sir Charles Igglesden's book *Those Superstitions*, published in 1932, an elderly midwife recounted:

Before the birth I always had a boy's nightshirt and a girl's nightgown quite ready […] If it was a boy I put on a girl's nightgown and if it was a girl I put on a boy's nightshirt […] And this is the reason […] The boy when he grew up would fascinate all girls, and a girl who had had a nightshirt put on her would have young men buzzing round her till she married.

Other superstitions such as not buying a cot for the baby until it is born and not revealing the chosen name until after the birth are still widely followed by parents to be, who still have enough fear of bad luck to practise them 'just in case'. Other rituals are followed although their origin has long since been forgotten; most parents string a rattle along the front of the pram to amuse their baby, but rattles were first used in this way not as a toy but in an effort to frighten away evil spirits.

Many Chinese boys are still given either a girl's name or they may be called after an animal. This is to protect them from devils who are thought to make attempts to injure male children. It is hoped that the 'milk name' will fool the devils, and is changed when the child reaches an age where he is considered to be safe.

As medical knowledge and technology increased during the twentieth century, the extent to which superstitions affected people's lives began to decline. While infant mortality rates were high, parents sought protection for their children in any way they could. They also sought protection for themselves and sometimes the baby was seen as a means of doing this. Sources reveal that the caul was still sought after well into the twentieth century. It was reported in the *Morning Post* of 9 June 1919:

Soon after the submarines got to work I was in the neighbourhood of the London docks and seeing in a shop a child's caul for sale I inquired the price. 'Three guineas,' said the man. I told him I had one for which I gave 1s. 6d. 'Yes, that was before the war […] the submarine had made life at sea so dangerous.'

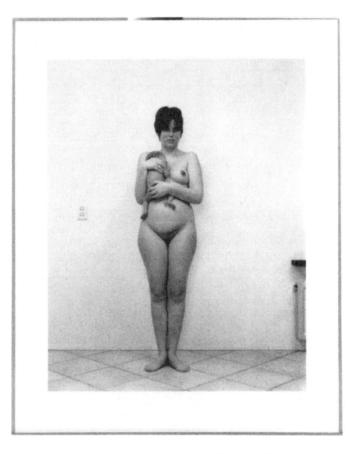

*Photo portrait by the Dutch artist Rineke Dijkstra
showing a mother and child one week after birth*

The Newborn Infant

Care of the newborn infant has come a long way since the early years of the twentieth century. As the century began, when a child was born, its survival was far from guaranteed. Before the emergence of specialised units a premature or unwell baby had to depend upon the strong instinct of the mother to provide the care needed to ensure its survival. Special Care Baby Units were only developed after the Second World War, when simple incubators were used to improve a tiny baby's chance of survival. Technology during the last fifty years has advanced to such an extent that incubators today have become precisely controlled microenvironments in which babies are monitored and treated.

Fear of death during the early part of the twentieth century still haunted every loving mother's subconscious. As late as 1911 'summer diarrhoea' claimed the lives of 32,000 babies under the age of one. As the years progressed the incidence of death from diarrhoea fell sharply, even before the introduction of refrigerators. This may be attributable to the disappearance of horse-drawn carriages and the consequent absence of horse manure from the streets. Horse droppings had always attracted large fly populations to the overcrowded, insanitary towns and the transmission of diseases was inevitable, particularly during the summer. While country children had a better chance of survival than those raised in the overcrowded towns, breast-fed babies remained the most likely to survive.

> I hope that my child, looking back on today,
> Will remember a mother who had time to play,
> Children grow up while you are not looking,
> There will be years ahead for cleaning and cooking,
> So quiet now cobwebs, dust go to sleep,
> I'm rocking my baby, and babies don't keep.
>
> – Anonymous

Breast or Bottle?

It is widely believed that the introduction of infant formula, which now closely resembles breast milk, has encouraged mothers to hand-feed their babies as the easy option since it takes time and patience to establish breast-feeding, but it is clear that some women have always been reluctant to breast-feed, finding the prospect unpleasant and sometimes even offensive. The difference is that in this modern age we are fortunate enough to be confident that if we choose to hand-feed our babies they will receive all the vitamins and minerals necessary to thrive and grow into healthy children.

During the first half of the twentieth century scientists focused a great deal of attention on the composition of human milk in an effort to imitate it as closely as possible. The first artificial formula milk was prepared by a German chemist in 1867 and was made primarily from milk, flour, potassium bicarbonate and malt. Towards the end of the nineteenth century some corporations such as Nestlé began to promote their 'safe and nutritious' alternative to breast milk. By 1911 condensed and evaporated milk were widely used for infant feeding and had the benefit of being a

Relief print of mother and child by the artist Eric Gill

cow's milk product that did not need to be kept cold. This milk was at least free from bacteria and nutritionally adequate – it was only during the 1920s that pasteurised bottled milk became readily available in England.

From the middle of the century American, Swiss and Japanese food technologists, in collaboration with chemists and paediatricians, managed to develop formula milk that contained all the essential nutrients of mother's milk. Their success, coupled with improved sanitary conditions and standards of living greatly improved the bottle-fed babies' chance of survival. At present infant formula manufacturers are continuing efforts to improve the composition of their milk. Their research involves efforts to replicate the trace elements and immunative ingredients and enzymes found in breast milk.

> There is no finer investment for any community than putting milk into babies.
>
> – Winston Churchill, 21 March, 1943

The improved safety of bottle-feeding has been blamed for the large number of artificially fed infants during the last few decades but it was not the only reason that breast-feeding remained unpopular. Urbanisation had its part to play as, with the lure of employment and without the support of extended families, women were less inclined to spend the time establishing a breast-feeding routine.

In the 1980s UNICEF and the World Health Organisation launched a worldwide campaign to encourage women to reject the advertising techniques from large conglomerates and to breast-feed their babies from birth for as long as possible.

In developing nations it is often impossible to prepare artificial feeds under hygienic conditions: bottles need to be sterilised and clean water is needed to make up the formula. UNICEF estimates that three million babies die each year because they are not breast-fed. Even in our developed nation tiny babies die as a result of the use of infected feeding apparatus. In some countries particular efforts are being made to discourage bottle-feeding by making it inconvenient. In Papua New Guinea, for example, a prescription is needed to buy a baby's bottle, and in the Philippines hospitals forbid the use of infant formula. As a result there has been a large reduction in their levels of infant mortality.

Although breast-feeding has gained more popularity in recent years there are still taboos in society that discourage many women from choosing to breast-feed. Many women are asked to cover up when breast-feeding in public, and often the only alternative is sitting in a public toilet to feed their baby. It is surprising in a society where nearly naked women in all sorts of poses are plastered over billboards for all, even children, to see, that nursing a young baby can arouse such shocked reactions.

Demand feeding is another area that has often aroused strong reactions and has been fiercely debated throughout history, with many contrasting opinions. The 1919 *Mothercraft Manual* was very strongly in favour of strict feeding schedules; mothers who gave in and fed their babies during the night were condemned as being weak-willed. In *Food Facts for Infants*, printed in the 1940s, mothers were encouraged to stick to the rigid feeding schedule and suggested that babies should not be fed between 10 p.m. and 6 a.m. Whether harassed mothers actually stuck to this rigid condition when their baby was howling with hunger during the night is difficult to know. Certainly these guidelines were followed by midwives; in *The Midwife's Tale* by Nicky Leap and Billie Hunter a midwife who began working in 1928 is quoted as saying:

> Demand feeding? Oh no, no – by the clock. Oh no, this demand feeding is a lot of nonsense! You take, for instance, yourself [...] You've got a baby, you've got a kitchen, you've got a husband. You've got dinner to get, you've got your washing to do, your ironing – how can you drop tools every five minutes and feed a baby? It's a lot of nonsense.

Midwives would take all the new arrivals to the hospital nursery each night to allow mothers an adequate rest, and as most women had a ten-day stay in hospital following birth, many found that once they arrived home their baby had already adjusted to a four-hourly routine, even those who were breast-fed. Some babies would be fed in the nursery using bottled breast milk that had been expressed from donor mothers.

Studies around the world have shown that in most non-industrial societies infants are fed frequently. The hunter-gatherer !Kung tribespeople of southern Africa feed their babies on average every thirteen minutes all day long and also frequently during the night. In other societies mothers have to adapt their feeding schedule to allow them to complete the tasks demanded of them. In the highlands of Nepal, for example, where women work in the rice fields and tend livestock, mothers feed their babies whenever they can snatch the opportunity. In Kenya mothers of the Gusii tribe usually leave young girls to care for their babies but return from work when called to nurse them. Others take the baby to work with them, carried in a sling where the breast is constantly available to the baby. Nestled close to the breast the baby is able to help itself.

The benefits of breast-feeding are now well known, and the medical profession is keen to encourage mothers to feed their own babies. In some societies around the world breast milk is considered to have symbolic power as well as nutritional benefits. In north-west Tunisia for example, the Khmir people believe that a vital life force is transferred from mother to child during feeding, via the milk. As commonly thought in Britain in past centuries, the Khmir people also believe that if a child is ill or badly behaved the mother is to blame as it is assumed that character passes through the milk.

Simple puréed food is often introduced soon after birth as a supplement to milk. Mothers in central Java supplement breast milk as early as three weeks after birth, and in the highlands of Thailand babies are also fed other foods after three weeks. Quechua mothers in Peru breast-feed on demand, but also provide broth for their infant soon after birth. The Amele of Papua New Guinea use soup, juice and mashed papaya as early supplements to milk.

Just as every woman's experience of birth is different, every woman seems to have very different feelings toward breast-feeding: some are repelled by the very idea of such intimate contact while others enjoy the experience to such an extent that they feel lost when their child no longer needs them for nourishment. Some women even reject physical advances from their partner during the period that they are breast-feeding because of their intense identification with their infant. They are so emotionally and physically attuned to their baby's needs that they resent interference from another person.

The Celebration of Birth

The birth of a baby is always a special event, and one that is celebrated all over the world. Although every culture and religion has a different way of honouring the occasion, family and friends are almost always invited to a feast of some kind, and gifts are presented to the new arrival. Some Christian churches baptise babies in holy water to cleanse the baby from sin and mark them as a follower of Jesus, therefore securing God's blessing. Through the application of water a child is transformed from one state to another, from original sinner to recipient of grace. Following the service family and friends are usually invited to a christening party where gifts, often made of silver, are then presented to the baby, and the christening cake, traditionally the top tier of the parents' wedding cake, is cut.

Other Christians, such as Jehovah's Witnesses and Baptists, do not believe in baptising babies, as babies are unable to make an informed decision as to whether they have chosen the correct path for themselves.

The explosion in medical knowledge and technology over the last half century has allowed today's parents to adopt a much more relaxed approach to rituals such as baptism, which now is often not arranged until well into the first year of a child's life, if at all. The number of babies being baptised has declined rapidly, although even some non-Christian parents still insist on baptising their children, in keeping with tradition.

A relatively new tradition that has gained popularity in recent years is a non-religious naming ceremony for a new baby, a way of celebrating the birth with family and friends and confirming the chosen name without involving religion.

One wept whose only child was dead,
Newborn, ten years ago.
'Weep not; he is in bliss,' they said,
She answered, 'Even so.
Ten years ago was born in pain
A child, not now forlorn.
But oh, ten years ago, in vain
A mother, a mother was born.

– Alice Meynell, 'Maternity', 1913

When a Chinese baby is born in the Taoist religion the time and date of the birth is written in eight Chinese characters called

Ba-zi. This is to facilitate the preparation of an accurate horoscope, in which great trust is placed and is used in later years to find a suitable marriage partner.

Horoscopes are also prepared for Hindu babies as soon as they are born. Following the birth the babies are washed and 'Om', meaning 'eternal', is written on their tongue with a gold pen dipped in honey. A priest then prepares a horoscope for the baby based on the exact time they were born. A name is given twelve days after the birth, and the baby is passed under and over a swinging cradle, once for each name chosen. The baby has its ears pierced during the first year, and at the end of this year the child's hair is completely shaved off in order to free them from evil.

In Algeria a baby's hair is cut following a celebration dinner where special traditional dishes are served to family and friends. The baby's hair is weighed, and the equivalent weight is given to the poor in gold or money. Then, to encourage breast-feeding, an older member of the family takes a date, chews it, then puts it on the baby's lips.

According to the Canadian and Greenlandic Inuit, when a person dies, a part of the spiritual essence of them, embodied in their name, is reincarnated in a newly born relative. Naming an infant after someone recently deceased means that certain personal qualities will be transferred from ancestor to child.

In many religions it is thought that the soul of a dead person rejuvenates itself in a new baby, sometimes in the same family. In some parts of Africa it is supposed that souls are reborn into the kin group to which they belonged in the previous life. Buddhists believe that a person's destiny relies on their behaviour in their previous life, with the good being rewarded by being reborn into a better life. Animals that are particularly virtuous may also be reincarnated as humans.

Eleventh-century illustration of the birth of Buddha

Newborn babies in Japan are taken to the temple where they are blessed and given presents in a ceremony known as *omiyamairi*. Baby girls are sometimes presented with a decorative kimono, often a gift from the grandmother, which is worn during the ceremony and kept for other special occasions in the child's life. When the baby is 100 days old the whole family gathers for a celebratory meal known as *kuizome* and the infant is given their 'first meal' from a special new bowl and tiny chopsticks.

Just as Christians use the element of water to confirm a child's path in life, so other cultures and religions use other basic elements to welcome their newborn children into the community. The Blood Indians of North America use the earth and the sun. An elder uses red ochre to mark the palm of the baby's hand and paint the tribal sign on the baby's face. He then shows the child to the sun in order to secure the child's future, ensuring they will always follow the light.

Australian Aborigines sometimes use fire to purify and protect a new infant. They make a fire of konkerberry leaves and twigs (konkerberry is known for its analgesic properties in traditional Aboriginal medicine), and then add bark and green leaves to make the fire smoke. Breast milk is squeezed onto the fire by the mother, and the grandmother passes the baby through the smoke. Participation of the grandmother signifies protection by the family, and the konkerberry leaves and twigs represent protection from the land.

Jewish parents welcome their boy babies into the community by the act of circumcision, following which the baby is also officially given a name. This is in accordance with God's law, and they believe it proves their intention to live a virtuous life. Interestingly, according to the Bible, circumcision must be carried out on the eighth day after birth, and scientists have recently discovered that a particular clotting factor in the blood reaches a peak on this day.

Choosing a Name

There is great diversity among the birth customs and traditions within each country and religion, but before most baby-welcoming ceremonies can take place parents have to face the task of choosing a name for the baby. A newborn baby is not necessarily an instant member of society, automatically accepted. His or her entry into the community is usually officially marked by a special ceremony, bestowing a chosen name. The Herero people of southern Africa announce a new arrival by a loud cry – 'Okauta', meaning 'little bow' when a boy is born, and 'Okazeu', the name of a bulb which is gathered and eaten, for a girl.

Western methods of name-giving have undergone many changes in the last two centuries. Before then it was a simple matter, the baby receiving the same name as the parent or an ancestor. During the Middle Ages parents had a comparatively small stock of Christian names to choose from, and relied almost entirely on fewer than two dozen names for each sex.

Nowadays the choice of names is almost endless and is more often determined by the taste of the parents, although there are still sometimes pressures from relations to name the baby according to family tradition or perhaps after a departed relative.

The Inuit often named their children after a dead relative, believing this would turn them into a true member of the family. The honour of naming the baby usually went to the mother or mother-in-law.

The Kayapo people of Brazil provide a child with an ancestral name in addition to the name given at birth. This special title is given to them during the festival of Bemp, when downy yellow parrot feathers are glued to the child's body and pale blue eggshells stuck to their head. In Mexico, Seri Indian babies are not named until their first birthday, and the people of the Dusin tribe in Borneo wait five years before naming their children; they fear the Devil will take the child from them if they do not fool him with a false name, thereby protecting the child during its most vulnerable years.

A Sikh baby's name is usually decided at a special service where the Guru Granth Sahib (the Sikh holy book) is opened at random and the first letter of the hymn at the top of the left-hand page is chosen as the first letter of the child's name.

In some Maasai communities parents hold a naming ceremony soon after the baby is born. The mother dresses in her best skirt of lambskin covered with beads and wears bead earrings and necklaces. A name is chosen by the elders and other women, and then the child is blessed with the words 'May that name dwell in you'.

In Hindu families the tenth day following birth is a memorable one for everyone. The infant is named and a cradle is made out of wood or straw. A silver belt, or piece of string in poorer families, is placed around the child's waist to monitor their growth. Children are often named after a grandparent or some object that signifies strength and purity. The choice of name is normally the responsibility of the elder members of the family.

For parents interested in numerology, the supposed value of a name in numerical terms, numerical implications need to be explored when choosing a name for the baby. Pythagoras, the sixth-century BC mathematical philosopher, placed great importance in numerology, and judged people by whether they had an odd or even number of vowels in their names.

The seventeenth-century writer Thomas Fuller stated that 'a name is a kind of face', concluding that a name seems to be a sum of personality. The importance of names can cause more than a few problems in some families, and trying to agree on a choice of name can sometimes be extremely difficult. A modern solution to this problem is often a compromise, where more than one Christian name is given. Before the eighteenth century the use of a middle name was very rare in Britain, and only a privilege of the more aristocratic and wealthy classes. Now a first name with no middle name is unusual. It is believed the practice reached the United Kingdom from France, where middle names were used as far back as the twelfth century.

Although some parents struggle to think of a suitable name for their infant, finding a name for a new member of the family need not always be a complicated affair. In some Native American tribes traditionally the father, emerging from the wigwam in which the newcomer has made their appearance, chooses a name from the first object that catches his eye, hence the Sioux chiefs Sitting Bull, Rain in the Face, Red Cloud and Spotted Tail.

Birth customs and traditions remain popular all over the world, although in some countries today and particularly in certain circumstances in the past, celebrations following the birth of a baby depended on the sex of the child. In poor communities the future of the family often depended on the child being a boy, and in some parts of the world this remains the case. A horrendous example of this is the dying rooms in China, where, as recently as 1995, baby girls were simply left to die so that the parents would be free to try for another child, hoping for a boy who would eventually be able to support the family.

In the absence of a natural son it is not uncommon for some Chinese families to adopt a boy. There are unofficial rules governing the adoption of a son in China. A man is supposed to select a child from any available on his father's side of the family. If there are none he must choose from among the descendants of his grandfather. If he is successful a lavish banquet is arranged during which all the elders place their signatures on a banner of red cloth, confirming the adoption. If the father is unable to adopt from within his own family and is forced to buy a child from outside, he must arrange an even larger banquet. Guests are then free to humiliate him by hurling insults about his inability to father a boy child.

– EPILOGUE –

CARE OF THE childbearing woman in Western society has come a long way since the days of the superstitious midwives and the barber-surgeons with their butcher's hooks. Women no longer have to fear being abandoned during labour with the baby half in, half out and no way of removing it. Severe blood loss and infections are not automatic death sentences, and although women remain anxious as they approach labour it is more from the fear of pain than fear of death.

As well as being able to cope with all the major problems associated with birth, the medical profession is now able to care for and treat the most tiny pre-term babies with considerable success. Parents now expect that problems experienced by their infant will be dealt with efficiently, even while the child is still in the womb.

The introduction of the contraceptive pill changed the lives of millions of women, giving them the freedom to control their own fertility for the first time ever. Unfortunately it seems that while women are now able to study for and enter almost any career they choose, once they become mothers they lose their value to society. Increasingly people are judged by how much money they earn, and one of the most important and difficult jobs in the world, that of motherhood, is also one of the most undervalued in our society.

Some women's groups have now placed this issue at the top of their agenda and are campaigning for women who stay at home to look after their children to be paid. They use International Women's Day to protest, and in the year 2000, women in 64 countries took part in strike action. They hope that in the future women will have a real choice as to whether to go back to work or stay at home to be with their children full time, free to make their decision without feeling financially pressured.

Governments at the present time, despite being keen to promote 'family values', invest large sums of money in nurseries in an attempt to allow mothers the opportunity of accepting employment, but will not invest in mothers who would prefer to spend valuable time with their children. If small children are able to enjoy the benefits of staying at home and forming close bonds with their mother, some feel that they will grow to become more secure and responsible adults, capable of interacting with others in a caring and positive manner.

Our ancestors would be staggered by the remarkable changes in the process of childbirth over the last one hundred years. Technology has armed scientists with the ability to create babies in test tubes and has even led to the possibility of cloning human beings in the near future. Since the beginning of investigations into the fertilisation of human ovum outside the womb the question of ethics has loomed large. The opportunities open to medical science are growing rapidly and many feel that just because scientists now have the ability to do something to help childless couples doesn't mean that it is morally right to do so.

Not only the concept, but also the actual process of IVF causes controversy: some embryos created in the test tube are not replanted into the womb of the mother; they are a by-product of the process. The centre of the debate focuses on the moral status of the fetus. Surplus embryos might be frozen or used for experimentation and for some this is a step too far.

The ethical and moral issues surrounding the rights of the unborn child, including those just a few days after fertilisation are complex and emotive. Who owns the created embryos? If the sperm and ova are donated by a husband and wife it is presumed that they are both dedicated to the production of a new life between them and have given informed consent, but what if their marriage breaks up and one partner withdraws their consent? Would a woman be within her rights to insist the embryos be implanted without agreement from her former husband? If embryos are transferred to the wrong mother, who has parental rights when the baby is born? The permutations are endless, resulting in extremely complicated ethical and legal considerations. Recent news stories have highlighted the emotional consequences for a couple when things go wrong.

Following the success of IVF comes the more far-reaching possibilities of altering the genetic structure of growing life and cloning. While further investigations into the development of the embryo and the formation of human life will lead, according to scientists, to a greater ability to understand and therefore avoid a host of genetic disorders, improve fertility, prevent miscarriage and produce new and improved methods of contraception, the complications and ethical dilemmas raised by genetic research has led to widespread concern. Cloning (asexual reproduction), ectogenesis (production outside of the body), genetic engineering (the control of hereditary defects or selection of preferred attributes by elimination or promotion of particular genes), and even hybridisation (interbreeding), are all areas that raise fundamental ethical issues and concerns which some find unacceptable to even contemplate.

The dilemmas surrounding childbirth today are very different from those faced by women living a hundred years ago. Couples today agonise over issues such as the ethics of prenatal testing and whether they would choose an abortion, however, perhaps our greatest fear for the future should be the deterioration of the role of the midwife in a society where technology is trusted more than humans. The dedicated personal care of one woman for another was all that women in the past could rely on, and while every woman has the right to the best care that modern medicine can offer, the value of this relationship should not be forgotten.

– FURTHER READING –

Chapter One – 'If We Could Survive Without a Wife ...' The Classical World

An exploration into the issues concerning fertility in the classical world is presented in detail in Angus McLaren's *History of Contraception from Antiquity to the Present Day*. An interesting book on the lives of women in ancient times is *Women in the Classical World* by E. Fantham et al., which offers an in-depth study of the status and experience of women in antiquity, and a helpful summary is contained in *Contraception and Abortion from the Ancient World to the Renaissance* by John M. Riddle.

Chapter Two – Holy Maidenhood: Motherhood in the Middle Ages

One of the most interesting discussions of the dangers associated with pregnancy and birth during this period is Trotula of Salerno's *Medieval Woman's Guide to Health*, edited and translated into modern English by Beryl Rowland. I also found *A Small Sound of the Trumpet: Women in Medieval Life* by Margaret Wade Labarge an informative and revealing account of women's experiences in medieval society. An exploration into the plight of women can also be found in *The Ties that Bound: Peasant Families in Medieval England* by Barbara Hanawalt, and *Medieval Women: Social History of Women in England 450–1500* by Henrietta Leyser offers a good overview.

Chapter Three – Birth Pangs: Mothers in Tudor and Stuart England

In *The Weaker Vessel*, Antonia Fraser examines women's lot during the seventeenth century. This book provides an intriguing insight into the perverse and conflicting views of women held by society, emanating largely from men of the cloth. David Cressy's *Birth, Marriage and Death* is an interesting and in-depth study containing many excerpts from historical diaries that vividly bring to life the common experiences of women living in Tudor and Stuart England. Due to the scarcity of historical records kept by women the majority of entries cited offer the male perspective, but despite this the fear and anxiety experienced by both partners as the day of delivery loomed is clearly evident.

Chapter Four – Taboo, Torment and Tragedy: The Eighteenth Century

The History of Infant Feeding from Elizabethan Times by David Forsyth and *A History of Infant Feeding* by Ian G. Wickes both examine the dangers involved in hand-rearing infants and provide a good overall view of the changes that led to the success of bottle-feeding. Books that I found of particular interest on the rearing of young infants and children were *Children in English Society* by Ivy Pinchbeck and Margaret Hewitt, and *The English Child in the Eighteenth Century* by R. Bayne-Powell. *A Lasting Relationship: Parents and Children over Three Centuries* by Linda Pollock is an anthology of extracts from letters, diaries and autobiographies of parents and children. This book offers intimate first-hand accounts that bring to life the history of children's experiences and shows that, despite their vastly different circumstances, they were in essence very much like children of today.

Chapter Five – 'If I Should Die ...' The Victorian Mother

Yesterday's Babies by Diana Dick offers an enlightening account of the dangers and difficulties associated with hand-rearing and examines the reluctance of many mothers to breast-feed. *Breasts, Bottles and Babies: A History of Infant Feeding* by Valerie A. Fildes is also very readable. A colourful and fascinating collection of illustrations and photographs of babies and the equipment used to care for them can be found in *Yesterday's Children: The Antiques and History of Childcare* by Sally Kevill-Davies. *The Changing Face of Childhood* by Gay Ochiltree and Don Edgar was useful in providing an overall picture of a child's lot and the events that shaped a better future for children.

Chapter Six – The Sweetness of Life: Twentieth-Century Birth

An interesting study of the changing role of the midwife can be found in *The Midwife's Tale* by Nicky Leap and Billie Hunter. This book contains first-hand accounts from 'old wives' who were keen to avoid being controlled by new regulations, and retells some of the experiences of women in their care. *Motherhood: From 1920 to the Present Day* edited by Vivien Devlin charts the changing experience of mothers over the past eighty years. Women from the ages of 15 to 93 are interviewed, and their views on pregnancy and childbirth build a remarkable picture of the varying expectations of motherhood across the generations.

FURTHER READING

A fascinating collection of antiques of childhood can be seen at:

The Museum of Childhood, Bethnal Green, London
The Museum of Childhood, Beaumaris, Anglesey
The Museum of Childhood, Sudbury, Derbyshire
The Museum of Childhood, Edinburgh

– BIBLIOGRAPHY –

Antoninus, *Confessionale*, ed. P. Ballerini (Verona, 1740)

Aristotle, *Historia Animalium*, ed. D. M. Balme (Cambridge University Press, 2002)

Aveling, James Hobson *English Midwives: Their History and Prospects* (J. A. Churchill, 1872)

Badinter, Elisabeth *The Myth of Motherhood: An Historical View of the Maternal Instinct* (Souvenir Press, 1981)
Baird, Sir Dugald interview on *Profile*, BBC Radio Scotland (1979)

Baldwin, J. W., *Masters, Princes and Merchants: The Social Views of Peter the Chanter and His Circle* (Princeton University Press, 1970)

Baumslag, Naomi and Dia L. Michels *Milk, Money and Madness: The Culture and Politics of Breastfeeding* (Greenwood Press, 1995)

Bayne-Powell, R., *The English Child in the Eighteenth Century* (John Murray, 1939)

Bernard, Christian Faust *Gedanken uber Hebammen und Hebammenanstalten auf dem Lande* (Frankfurt, 1784)

Biller, P. P. A., 'Birth Control in the West in the Thirteenth and Early Fourteenth Centuries', *Past and Present* 94 (1982)

Bissell-Pope, Williard (ed.) *The Diary of Benjamin Robert Haydon* (Harvard University Press, 1963)

Brome, R., *Antipodes IIV* (1640)

Brook, Danae *Naturebirth: Preparing for Natural Birth in an Age of Technology* (Penguin, 1976)

Burger, Lisbeth *Vierzig Jahre Storchentante: Aus dem Tagebuch einer Hebamme* (Breslau, 1936)

Cadogan, W., *Essay upon Nursing and the Management of Children: From Their Birth to Three Years of Age* (1748)

Camp, John *Magic, Myth and Medicine* (Taplinger Publishing Co., 1973)

Carlile, Richard *Every Woman's Book* (London, 1826)

Carter, Robert Brudenell *On the Pathology and Treatment of Hysteria* (London,1853)

Chamberlain, Mary *Old Wives' Tales: Their History, Remedies and Spells* (Virago Press, 1981)

Chaucer, Geoffrey *The Canterbury Tales*, trans. Nevill Coghill (Penguin, 1977)

Chesler, *Ellen Woman of Valor: Margaret Sanger and the Birth Control Movement in America* (Simon & Schuster, 1992)

Chisholm, J. J., 'Swaddling, Cradleboards and the Development of Children', *Early Human Development* 2 (1978)

Cressy, David *Birth, Marriage and Death: Ritual, Religion and the Life-Cycle in Tudor and Stuart England* (Oxford University Press, 1997)

Crook, J. A., *Law and Life of Rome* (Thames & Hudson, 1967)

DeLee, Joseph B., 'The Prophylactic Forceps Operation', *American Journal of Obstetrics and Gynecology* 1 (1920)

Demause, Lloyd (ed.) *The History of Childhood* (Souvenir Press, 1976)

Devlin, Vivien (ed.) *Motherhood: From 1920 to the Present Day* (Polygon, 1995)

Dick-Read, Grantly *Childbirth Without Fear* (William Heinemann Medical Books, 1942)

Dictionary of Daily Wants (Houlston & Wright, 1860)

Domiciliary Midwifery and Maternity Bed Needs Peel Report (HMSO, 1970)

Erickson, Carolly *Anne Boleyn* (Macmillan, 1984)

Fantham, E., H. P. Foley, N. B. Kampden, S. B. Pomeroy, and H. A. Shapiro, *Women in the Classical World* (Oxford University Press, 1995)

Final Report of the Departmental Committee on Maternal Mortality and Morbidity (HMSO, 1932)

Ford, C. S., *A Comparative Study of Human Reproduction* (Yale University Press, 1945)

Forel, August *Sexual Ethics*, trans. C. F. Marshall (1908)

Forsythe, David 'The History of Infant Feeding from Elizabethan Times', *Proceedings of the Royal Society of Medicine* 4 (1910–1911)

Fraser, Antonia *The Weaker Vessel: Woman's Lot in Seventeenth-Century England* (Weidenfield & Nicholson, 1984)

Fulford, Roger (ed.) *Dearest Mama: Private Correspondence of Queen Victoria & the Crown Princess of Prussia 1861–1864* (Evans, 1977)

Furnivall, F. J. (ed.) *Hali Meidenhad* (Early English Text Society, 1969)

Galen, *De temperamentis*, ed. J. F. Payne (Cambridge, 1881)

Garnet, Richard S. J., *The Book of Oaths* (London, 1689)

Gathorne-Hardy, J., *The Rise and Fall of the British Nanny* (Hodder & Stoughton, 1972)

Geddes, P. and J. A. Thomson *The Evolution of Sex* (London, 1889)

Gordon, Alexander *Treatise on the Epidemic Puerperal Fever of Aberdeen* (1795)

Graham, Harvey *Eternal Eve* (Hutchinson, 1950)

Green, Shirley *The Curious History of Contraception* (Ebury Press, 1971)

Griffith, Frederick 'Instruments for the Production of Abortion sold in the Marketplace of Paris', *Medical Record* 30/11 (1904)

Gruner, O. Cameron *A Treatise on the Canon of Avicenna, Incorporating a Translation of the First Book* (Luzac & Co, 1930)

Hall, Ruth (ed.) *Dear Dr Stopes: Sex in the 1920s* (Penguin, 1978)

Hamilton, Alexander *A Treatise on Midwifery, Comprehending the Whole Management of Female Complaints, and the Treatment of Children in Early Infancy. To Which are Added Prescriptions for Women and Children* (Dickson, Creech & Elliot, 1781)

Hanawalt, Barbara *The Ties that Bound: Peasant Families in Medieval England* (Oxford University Press, 1986)

Helmholz, R., *Marriage Litigation in Medieval England* (Cambridge University Press, 1974)

Herlihy, D., *Medieval Households* (Harvard University Press, 1985)

Himes, Norman Edwin *The Medical History of Contraception* (Gamut Press, 1963)

Hodge, A. T., *Roman Aqueducts and Water Supply* (Duckworth, 1992)

Inglis, Brian *A History of Medicine* (World Publishing Co., 1965)

Ingpen, Robert and Philip Wilkinson *A Celebration of Customs and Rituals of the World* (Dragon's World, 1994)

Josceline, Elizabeth *The Mother's Legacy to her Unborn Child* (1625)

Kevill-Davies, Sally *Yesterday's Children: The Antiques and History of Childcare* (Antique Collectors Club Ltd, 1991)

Knappen, M. M. (ed.) *Two Elizabethan Puritan Diaries by Richard Rogers and Samuel Ward* (SPCK, 1933)

Kurzgefasste Gedanken von dem Verdebeten Zustande des Hebammen (Lubeck, 1752)

Labarge, Margaret Wade *A Small Sound of the Trumpet: Women in Medieval Life* (Beacon Press, 1986)

Latham, Robert and William Matthews (eds.) *Diary of Samuel Pepys (G. Bell & Sons, 1970–1983)*

Leap, Nicky and Billie Hunter *The Midwife's Tale: An Oral History from Handywoman to Professional Midwife* (Scarlet Press, 1993)

Lefkowitz, Mary R., *Heroines and Hysterics* (St Martin's Press, 1981)

Leven and Melville Papers (Scottish Record Office, GD 26/401/29)

Leyser, Henrietta *Medieval Women: Social History of Women in England 450–1500* (Weidenfeld & Nicolson, 1995)

MacFarlane, A., 'Variations in Number of Births and Perinatal Mortality by Day of the Week in England and Wales', *British Medical Journal* 2 (1978)

MacFarlane, Alan (ed.) *The Diary of Ralph Josselin 1616–1683* (Oxford University Press, 1976)

Markale, Jean *Women of the Celts* (Cremonesi, 1975)

Marsh, A., *Ten Pleasures of Marriage* (1682)

McLaren, Angus *A History of Contraception from Antiquity to the Present Day* (Basil Blackwell Ltd, 1990)

McLeish, Kenneth *Myths and Legends of the World* (Bloomsbury, 1998)

Mattingly, Garrett (ed.) *Calendar of State Papers*, IV part 2 (1947)

Miller, Douglas 'Observations in Unsuccessful Forceps Cases', *British Medical Journal* (1928)

Munro Kerr, J. M., R. W. Johnstone and M. H. Phillips (eds.)

Historical Review of Obstetrics and Gynaecology 1800–1950 (E & S Livingstone, 1954)

Nichols, R. H. and F. A. Wray *The History of the Foundling Hospital* (Oxford University Press, 1935)

Noonan, J. T., *Contraception: A History of Its Treatment by the Catholic Theologians and Canonists* (Belknap, 1965)

Odent, Michael *Entering the World: The De-Medicalisation of Childbirth* (Marion Boyars, 1984)

On Perinatal and Neonatal Mortality The Short Report, House of Commons Paper 663S1 (HMSO, 1980)

Oribasius, 'Librium Incertum' in U. C. Busse and C. Daremberg (eds.) *Oeuvres D'oribase, Collections des medecins Grec et Latin* (Paris, 1851–1877)

Pinchbeck, Ivy and Margaret Hewitt *Children in English Society* (Routledge & Kegan Paul, 1969)

Plato, *Laws*, trans. by A. E. Taylor (J. M. Dent & Sons, 1934)

Pollock, Linda *A Lasting Relationship: Parents and Children Over Three Centuries* (University Press of New England, 1987)

Pomeroy, Sarah B., *Women as Midwives and Physicians in the East* (Oxford University Press, 1999)

Price, F. D., 'The Commission for Ecclesiastical Causes within the Dioceses of Bristol & Gloucester, 1574', *Transactions of the Bristol & Gloucestershire Archaeological Society*, 59 (1937)

Raynalde, Thomas *The Birth of Mankynde* (1545)

Riddle, John M., *Contraception and Abortion from the Ancient World to the Renaissance* (Harvard University Press, 1992)

Robert of Flamborough *Liber Poenitentialis*, ed. J. J. Francis (Pontifical Institute of Medieval Studies, 1971)

Rowland, Beryl (ed.) *Medieval Woman's Guide to Health* (Kent State University Press, 1981)

Rueff, Jacob *The Expert Midwife* (London, 1637)

Scott, Sir Walter *Letters on Demonology & Witchcraft* (NY Citadel Press, 1970)

Shorter, Edward *A History of Women's Bodies* (Basic Books, 1982)

Smellie, William *A Treatise on the Theory and Practice of Midwifery* (London, 1752)

Smith, H., *Letters to a Married Woman* (1792)

Soranus, *Gynaecology,* ed. Owsei Temkin (Baltimore University Press, 1956)

Steinem, Gloria *The Verbal Karate of Florynce R. Kennedy, Esq.* (Holt, Rhinehart & Winston, 1973)

Stewart, Duncan *Medical Essays and Observations, 1752: The Caesarean Operation Done with Success by a Midwife* (1752)

Stone, Laurence *The Family, Sex and Marriage in England 1500–1800* (Weidenfeld & Nicolson, 1977)

Stopes, Marie *Married Love* (1918; Gollancz,1995)

Storey, Matthew (ed.) *Two East Anglian Diaries 1641–1729: Isaac Archer and William Coe* (Boydell & Brewer, 1994)

Strickland, Irina *The Voices of Children* 1700–1914 (Basil Blackwell, 1973)

Tenon, Jacques Rene *Mémoires Sur Les Hopitaux de Paris* (1788)

Thomas of Chobham, *Summa Confessorum*, ed. F. Broomfield (Louvain, 1968)

Thomson, Flora *Lark Rise to Candleford* (Oxford University Press, 1939)

Weekley, Ernest *Dictionary of First Names, including Jack and Jill* (Tiger Books, 1994)

Welldon, Estela V., *Mother, Madonna, Whore: The Idealisation and Denigration of Motherhood* (Free Association Books, 1988)

White, Charles *Treatise on the Management of Pregnancy and Lying-*

in Women, and the Means of Curing, but more especially of Preventing the Principal Disorders to which they are Liable (1772)

Wickes, Ian G., 'A History of Infant Feeding', *Archives of Disease in Childhood* 28 (1953)

William of Pagula *The Oculus Sacerdotis* (1331)

Willis, Roy G., *World Mythology* (Simon & Schuster, 1993)

Willughby, Percival *Observations in Midwifery* (c. 1670; S. R. Publishers, 1972)

Woodham-Smith, Cecil *Queen Victoria, Her Life and Times 1819–1861* (Hamish Hamilton, 1972)

Scurvy

How a Surgeon, a Mariner and a Gentleman Solved the Greatest Medical Mystery of the Age of Sail
by Stephen R. Bown

£9.99 • hardback • 1 84024 357 0 • 179 x 129 mm/288 pp

The fascinating story of the greatest medical mystery of the Age of Sail.

In the days of the tall ships, one dreaded foe was responsible for more deaths at sea than piracy, shipwreck and all other illnesses combined. Cruelly culling sailors and stunting maritime enterprise, this plague of the seas was Scurvy. Countless mariners suffered an agonising death that began with bleeding gums, wobbly teeth, and the opening of old wounds.

A cure had eluded doctors and philosophers since the time of the ancient Greeks, but in the late eighteenth century surgeon James Lind, the great sea captain James Cook, and physician Sir Gilbert Blane undertook to crack the riddle of Scurvy. Their timely discovery, just as Napoleon was mobilising for the conquest of Europe, solved the greatest medical mystery of the Age of Sail and irrevocably altered the course of world events.

This is a history and a detective story about class, wilful ignorance and ludicrous decision-making; and about how a cure for Scurvy was found, ignored, lost, and finally implemented to the great benefit of all seafaring nations.

Lipstick on the Noose

Martyrs, Murderesses and Madwomen
by Geoffrey Abbott

£9.99 • hardback • 1 84024 367 8 • 179 x 129 mm/288 pp

The ultimate collection of grisly tales from the gallows, guillotine and gas chamber in which the fairer sex gets it in the neck …

From the tragic fate of Queen Marie Antoinette, who bravely faced the guillotine in front of a screaming mob, to the hastily improvised hanging of a sadistic mother and daughter team, *Lipstick on the Noose* is brimming with macabre true stories of executed women from around the world.

Interspersed with quirky anecdotes both tragic and comic, plus contemporary illustrations, this is history at its most morbidly fascinating.

Geoffrey Abbott served for many years as a Yeoman Warder (Beefeater) at the Tower of London. Author of 16 books including the bestselling *The Executioner Always Chops Twice* and contributor to the Encyclopedia Britannica, he has made numerous television appearances.

www.summersdale.com